ALL BUT ME AND THEE

CONTENTS

PROLOGUE 7

Chapter 1
NERVOUS IN THE SERVICE 11

Chapter 2
RACKING UP THE 8-BALLS 23

Chapter 3
THE CHICKEN OR THE EGG 39

Chapter 4
WHITE MAGIC 55

Chapter 5
DOUBLE OR NOTHING 71

Chapter 6
GANGPLANK FEVER 89

Chapter 7
PASS ALONG THE BUCK 107

Chapter 8
GI PSYCHIATRY 123

Chapter 9
GIDEON'S THREE HUNDRED MEN 141

Chapter 10
FEMALE OF THE SPECIES 159

Chapter 11
THAT PIECE OF PAPER 177

Chapter 12
THREE IN ONE 191

Chapter 13
THE PAY OFF 205

ALL BUT ME AND THEE

Psychiatry at the Foxhole Level

By

BRIGADIER GENERAL ELLIOT D. COOKE

WASHINGTON

INFANTRY JOURNAL PRESS

COPYRIGHT 1946 BY
ELLIOT D. COOKE

FIRST EDITION
NOVEMBER 1946

PROLOGUE

Of any who read these pages, I ask indulgence. The events described herein did not happen exactly as depicted, but in essence they are factual and the results of an official inquiry. If my treatment of them appears too flippant for the more serious minded, assurance is offered that no slights are intended, nor is the subject itself meant to be taken lightly. It is merely my own style of writing, and probably the only style of which I am capable. Indeed, it was for that very reason this book was attempted, so that those with no more technical skill or knowledge than myself might share with me some insight and understanding of one of the greatest problems ever presented to our people. What I have learned regarding this problem came the hard way, but only because of my own delimitations, and not because I did not receive both encouragement and help from the people to whom I now offer my sincerest thanks and acknowledgment, to wit:

Brigadier General William C. Menninger, Chief of the Psychiatric Division of The Surgeon General's Office, and his most able and amiable assistant, Lieut. Colonel Norman Q. Brill, both of whom not only encouraged me in this meager effort of mine, but also did their best to keep me straight on technical details and phraseology.

Major Generals Norman D. Kirk and David N. W. Grant, Surgeon General and Air Surgeon, respectively, who, while perhaps at times, were amused at my temerity, nevertheless, made all facilities available for my official inquiry on which the book is based.

Major General Howard McC. Snyder, who actually supervised the technical side of this inquiry, together with five most eminent psychiatrists who assisted him, namely: Dr. C. Charles Burlingame, Dr. Edward A. Strecker, Dr. Frank Fremont-Smith, Dr. Karl M. Bowman and Dr. Harry C. Solomon, all of whom gave me instructions in more fields than one.

Colonel Westray Battle Boyce, the determined little Wac who never abandoned her earnest efforts to bring order out of the chaos of our staff conferences.

"Trigger," "Will," and "Dave," who flew to the far corners of the world to supplement the efforts of Ralph Bing and myself.

And last, but not least, my ever-loving wife, "Jack," who bore patiently with me during my anguished hours of composition.

Of them, also, I ask indulgence should my story seem less worthy than their hopes.

ALL BUT ME AND THEE

Chapter 1

Nervous In The Service

~~~~~~

Secret weapons did not cause the only surprises in World War II. London's bewilderment over the first buzz-bomb was no greater than the consternation of our own General Staff in the spring of 1943 when the news suddenly burst upon it that nearly as many men were being discharged from the Army as were entering through induction stations. The number of these discharges was enough to alarm even the most complacent because it was well up into six figures. In fact, over a given period of time, more men were getting out of the Army than were being sent across the Pacific to fight Japs. It is small wonder then that the Chief of Staff wanted to be informed immediately how such a thing could come about.

Well, he and the rest of the staff soon found out. An unknown menace was knocking at our door; something new had arisen, a thing called "psychoneurosis." The word alone hit us with the unexpectedness of one of Mr. Schicklgruber's flying dingbats, and caused just as much dismay. Even more so, in fact, because Hitler's bombs were self-explanatory, but who knew what a neurosis was or where it came from?

Certainly, I, for one, had no idea. Off and on, during some thirty years' service, I had attended my share of military schools, had commanded troops in battle and even, at one time, had been able to recite my general orders without mistake, but in 1943 I didn't know enough about psychoneurosis to find the word in a dictionary. Consequently, though not entirely alone in my ignorance, it was with some surprise that I found myself detailed as a member of the committee assigned to determine just what psychoneurosis was, how it had managed to infiltrate into the Army, and what should be done about it.

Later, I learned the reason for my assignment. It seems we had plenty of Army medicos practicing psychiatry, but many of them disagreed among themselves, and usually their reports, both oral and written, were completely over the heads of the average line officer. Therefore, by adding me, a Doughboy, to the group of eminent specialists called in to investigate the situation, it was hoped, a rather forlorn hope, perhaps, that I might find out enough to present the subject on what might be called the foxhole level.

There are many who will say such a thing is impossible. They will contend that no one without a medical education could even approach an understanding of psychiatry, that a fair percentage of practicing physicians don't know what it's all about, and that any dabbling on the part of such as I would be the same as practicing medicine without a license. On the other hand, there are some—my friends, perchance—who might insist that if a guy like me could understand such a subject, anybody could. Be that as it may, I was, by order, about to seek the neurosis in its lair and my first act was to get another infantryman, Colonel Ralph Bing, to assist me.

Ralph and I had served together on several Army posts, and I knew he possessed a lot of common sense along with plenty of experience in handling soldiers. He had only one weakness, so far as I was concerned. In peacetime he preferred playing polo to golf, and usually could be found in command of a service company or other infantry organization connected with horses and stables. But he was smarter than I in one respect. Right from the start Ralph could spell psychoneurosis without looking it up!

It was Ralph who pointed out my first blunder. We had attended our first conference with a group of staff medicos, and most of the terms used were so technical I could only understand a few. I noticed Ralph got fidgety over each question I asked, and I thought he, too, was having difficulty in understanding the phraseology. After the meeting I found it was for another reason.

"Listen, Cookie," he said, "the name for those doctors is psychia*trists*, t-r-i-s-t-s."

"Well, how did I pronounce it?"

"You kept calling them psychia*tricks*, and I don't think they liked it."

Naturally, I was embarrassed. Not wanting to show further ignorance in the future, I sought out my friend, Bill Shambora. Bill was Surgeon of the Army Ground Forces, and also a graduate of our best military schools. I knew he would be amused by some of my questions, but I needed information.

"What," I asked him, "is the difference between a psychiatrist and a neuropsychiatrist?" I had heard both terms used.

Bill was amused, all right, and likewise cautious.

"Don't go around quoting me," he warned, "but to put it briefly, a psychiatrist is a specialist who deals with mental disorders, while a neuropsychiatrist handles cases that are both nervous and mental or are on the borderline between the two."

"I get it. If I mistook a neuropsychiatrist for a plain psychiatrist, he'd be offended, but if I call 'em by the top title, everyone will be satisfied. Now tell me what a Freudist is."

"Freudian is the word," Bill corrected me. "It means a person who believes in Sigmund Freud's theory that certain kinds of nervous disorders and dreams are based upon unconscious sexual repressions, and the cure is to bring them from the unconscious to the conscious. The symbolic forms of suppressed wishes. . . ."

"Hold it right there," I begged. "You mean a guy gets sick because of some sex urge he doesn't know he has, but if a doctor can help him realize what the urge is, he may be cured?"

"That sounds a little crude, but it's the general idea."

"Then would one psychiatrist be hinting at a sex angle if he called another psychiatrist a 'coucher'?"

"No. And it wouldn't be ethical, either."

I knew that medical ethics were inviolate, but I had to find some path out of the quagmire of words confusing me, so I persisted.

"Well, I heard one, just the same, so come on and tell me what it means."

Bill was reluctant at first, but finally gave in.

"There are a good many neuropsychiatrists who believe that better results can be accomplished by what they call 'free association'; that means their patients must be completely relaxed and not sitting face to face with the psychiatrist. So those doctors have a quiet, well appointed room, not at all like an office, where they hold their interviews, which consist mostly of having their patients recline on a couch and talk about anything that comes into their mind, such as their childhood, sex life, and so on. That's where the term 'coucher' comes from. Probably originated through jealousy on someone's part."

"Yeah, I can see where jealousy might come into it, all right. But how about the couchees or couchesses? What brings them to the supine position like that ?"

"Why," Bill was surprisingly patient, "they are people with some kind of a subconscious idea that is suppressed and painful enough to cause a mental disturbance or functional nervous disorder. They are psychoneurotics."

"Well," I sighed, "that just about brings me back to where I started. But thanks a lot. I'm going out to see what some of these guys look like with the subconscious ideas."

It was not difficult to find psychoneurotics to look at because every military hospital in the land had a neuropsychiatric or NP ward, as they were called, and most of them were crowded to capacity. With one or more hundred to choose from, Ralph and I selected the hospital at Camp Blanding for our first visit. We found it had one "locked" ward and three "open" wards for NP patients.

Our interest regarding inmates of the locked ward was purely academic. The inquiry in which we were engaged was in no way intended to question, in the slightest degree, the diagnosis of any doctor. If a medical officer thought it necessary to confine a patient for his own, or other people's safety, that was final, so far as we were concerned.

None of the men we saw in the locked wards appeared at all violent. One was quietly playing cards with a nurse, and did not even look up as we came by. He had three times attempted suicide because he believed his wife was being untrue to him. He didn't have any proof, he just thought she was.

Another lad came up to tell me that he had lost the sight of one eye and feared he would soon be totally blind. Actually, the doctors could find no disease in either eye. As we talked, the psychiatrist who accompanied us raised the boy's arms, first one and then the other, to various heights, and the lad remained in each position until the doctor changed it. As we started off, the patient remained perfectly still with arms extended like semaphores until the doctor stepped back and pulled the boy's arms down a normal position.

With a third patient the doctor was more prudent.

"Don't make any sudden moves," he cautioned me.

"Why?" I asked, regarding the pajama-clad figure before us.

The man seemed docile enough, although there was a vacant look in his somewhat glazed eyes.

"Conditioned reflexes," the doctor explained, "reacts unexpectedly. Last time I reached out too quickly to take his pulse and he knocked me clear across the room."

No doubt existed in my mind that such men were certainly in need of medical attention. Also, I could see by the expression on Ralph's face that he agreed with my feeling that he and I were completely out of our sphere of activity in so far as locked-ward patients were concerned. But in the open wards it was quite different. There we found the kind of psychoneurotics we were looking for.

A hundred or more patients were loafing around in hospital suits, talking, reading, or playing games. They didn't act any sicker than I did. As a group, they seemed just about like any other collection of soldiers. I spoke to one of the more intelligent looking ones.

"What's wrong with you, soldier?"

He stared at me defiantly.

"I'm queer," he stated flatly, meaning he was a homosexual.

The next one had pains in his back. He showed me where they started, at the base of the spine, spreading to the stomach and into the groin. As he talked, he acted as though the pains were actually occurring, although I had seen him in a friendly roughhouse with another patient, as we entered the ward.

"Hysteria type," the psychiatrist informed me.

A Negro had the same ailment, but a different word for it.

"I'se got the misery," he said, holding his hands to the small of his back.

And that's what a lot of them had; a pain in the back or pain in the head, shooting pains for which the doctors could find no organic cause. There were also some hypochondriacs—men having a morbid fear of disease, and who identify every slight pain as the symptom of a serious illness—some plain everyday bedwetters and a large number of what a ward doctor called the anxiety type.

He went on to explain to me that men in this latter group were troubled with feelings of apprehension, uncertainty and fear. At night they had disquieting dreams; during the day they worried constantly about their families, financial affairs, or how they were getting along on their jobs. In fact, they worried about anything or everything, depending upon the individual. While this information was being imparted to me, Ralph had conducted his own independent inspection of the patients. When we met outside the wards he wore a puzzled frown.

"Are those what they call psychoneurotics?" he asked me.

"They seem to be. Why?"

"Why? Well, for Pete's sake. They are about the only kind of soldiers I ever had in the service companies I've commanded, but I didn't know what they were called."

"You mean in the service company you got all the eight balls the other company commanders in the regiment wanted to get rid of?"

"Sure. And that's what those guys are I just saw!"

"As a psychiatrist," injected the doctor who had shown us around, "I am not prepared to concede that they are eight balls."

Sensing the possibility of a prolonged debate, I suggested we repair to the comforts of the Officers' Club, where we could conduct our discussion with the aid of a cold drink. I knew Ralph's statements were true, yet I was none too sure of their significance.

"Now," I said to our doctor guide, as soon as we had our feet stretched out and ice tinkling in our respective glasses, "you say those men are sick?"

"That is correct," replied the psychiatrist. "They're sick."

"And too sick to do any duty," said Ralph, a little bitterly.

"On the contrary, I think nearly all of them could perform some kind of duty."

"What!" Ralph and I exclaimed simultaneously.

The Doc took a long swig, his eyes smiling at us over the top of his glass. Then he leaned forward.

"Let me put it this way. If you assigned each one of those men to the kind of work he wanted to do, or was qualified for, and permitted him to work when he pleased, you wouldn't see any of them over there in the wards."

Ralph and I looked at each other in amazement.

"If they could do that," I protested, "you wouldn't see them in the Army, either."

"True," the Doc admitted succinctly, "consequently, they are in a hospital."

It took me a minute or two to get that through my head. Then I got mad.

"Why, you're just catering to a bunch of malingerers!"

The Doc carefully tamped out his cigarette.

"General," he said, "you have the rank to say that, but actually you don't know what you're talking about."

For a minute I was so startled I couldn't think. Then I got ready to pin his ears back. And then I suddenly realized he was speaking the truth.

"O.K.," I said, settling back, "you tell me where I'm wrong."

It was his turn to be surprised. But the Doc was no panty-waist.

"Very well," he said, "consider those men with pains in their backs. Regardless of how it came about, they were admitted to this hospital. All right, they were put through the clinic, X-rayed, blood tested and all the rest of it, but no organic disease could be found. Still they had pains in their backs. So they are sent to me for observation, diagnosis and treatment."

The Doc took another drink.

"Whether you believe it or not, I can assure you those men suffer with the pains they complain about. You say they are malingerers and merely pretend to be sick. But, after ten years of practicing psychiatry, I am confident I can tell the difference between a person who is suffering from pain and one who is not."

Ralph and I consulted each other with our eyes. We were thinking the Doc's manner was convincing, even if his words didn't seem to be.

"Let me ask you this," ventured Ralph, "does it require a psychiatrist to tell the difference between a malingerer and a psychoneurotic, or could it be done by a general medical officer?"

"Depends upon the officer. Most of those I've seen in the Army might find it difficult to do so. In any event, I think the majority of them would prefer the opinion of a specialist."

"And whether or not a person is psychoneurotic can't be proved by X-ray, blood test, microscope or test tube. It's all a matter of judgment on the part of a psychiatrist?"

"Yes, and that is why they have psychiatrists in the Army."

"Yeah," I put in, "and that's also why we have hospitals full of psychoneurotics."

The Doc regarded me with surprise.

"You surely don't believe I go out looking for patients, do you?"

"Well, you've got them."

"I've got them, is right," he admitted, a little sadly. "But I try to get rid of them as soon as possible."

"How?"

"Immediately they improve, I return them to duty," the Doc looked pensive for a moment, "the only trouble is, they keep getting back into the hospital."

"What do you do then?"

"Finally, if I can't find any other way, I discharge them on a certificate of disability."

There it was! The very thing causing all the disturbance.

"Sure," I said, "and they go right out and get a pension."

"Oh, no," the Doc was greatly pained, "in the majority of cases I mark them, 'Line of duty, NO,' because they undoubtedly were psychoneurotic before they came in the Army."

"That doesn't make any difference," I said, crossly. "We have been told that the Veterans Bureau makes its own decisions in such cases, and that about ninety per cent of all men discharged as psychoneurotics have applied for a pension, and most of them are getting one, too."

The Doc was horrified, and Ralph took advantage of that fact, in an effort to trip him up.

"If those men were psychoneurotic before they came into the service, how is it the psychiatrists at induction stations didn't know it and reject them in the first place?

"They do," said the Doc, recovering quickly, "and we have an induction station right here on the post. We might go see the psychiatrist there, if you're interested."

We were interested all right, although I was already beginning to regret ever having heard the word psychoneurosis. But whether I liked it or not, there was a hell of a problem to solve and it was my job, so we went to the induction station.

The psychiatrist at the induction station wore glasses, took his job most seriously, and appeared somewhat morose. Later, Ralph confided to me that he thought "Gloomy Gus," as he called him, looked more like a psychoneurotic than most of the patients we had seen in the hospital. However, Gloomy Gus furnished us with some interesting data.

CHAPTER 2

RACKING UP THE 8-BALLS

~~~~~~

JIMMY-THE-HARD WAS A TOUGH GUY! ONE OF THE ROOTIN'
tootin' kind that never seemed to need more than five hours
sleep himself, and who spent most of his waking hours making
sleep more or less impossible for his subordinates. His infantry
division was rated one of the best, and had been commended
highly in the Louisiana maneuvers. And nearly a thousand men
from that same division were in hospitals as psychoneurotics!

Ralph Bing and I had not been on the job long enough to
have learned much but, even so, we certainly thought we knew
more about psychoneurotics than Jimmy-the-Hard. Unfortunately, Jimmy didn't agree with us.

"Are you trying to tell me how to run my division?" he
shouted when I pointed out the large number of casualties
charged to his organization. "Of course I got rid of those weaklings. How do you think I'm going to fight a war with people
like that? This is a man's outfit."

"The trouble is, General," I said, "the hospitals are getting so
full of psychoneurotics that pretty soon we won't have room for
anybody else."

"Take them out and put them in labor battalions. Make them
work; earn their keep. Nothing the matter with those men that
any good first sergeant can't cure—out behind the orderly
room."

"General," I asked gently, "don't *you* have any good first
sergeants?"

Jimmy's blood pressure went up like a P-38.

"Don't be ridiculous," he snapped back at me. "Of course I

23

have. And I also have about fifteen thousand other boys to look after. They're good, honest kids, not knowing what they are going up against, but doing their best just the same. The more and better training they get now, the fewer will be killed or wounded later on. Which would you rather have me do: Use my best noncommissioned officers to train those youngsters, or use them to ride herd on a bunch of wet-nosed brats who wouldn't fight a rabbit?"

"It isn't entirely a matter of courage, General." I hastened to air some of my newly acquired knowledge of psychiatry. "The doctors have assured us that those men are sick."

"Then let the doctors take care of them. That's what doctors are for."

"But the men you got rid of were not so sick they couldn't do some kind of work," Ralph objected. "They'd be all right in a service company. I know in some of the companies I've commanded . . ."

"Not in my division," Jimmy-the-Hard interrupted, bringing both hands down on his desk with a bang. "I have a training schedule to meet. Every man must be able to shoot a gun, hike twenty-five miles in eight hours and go through the obstacle and infiltration courses. Give me men who can do that and I'll make soldiers of them."

I wanted to point out that he might be making psychoneurotics out of the ones he didn't turn into soldiers, but it hardly seemed worthwhile. Jimmy wouldn't have cared if he was.

"May we see the division surgeon?" I asked, thinking Jimmy's senior medical officer would be more understanding and much easier to talk to.

"See anybody you like," said Jimmy, reaching for a phone.

But the surgeon was not in his office. It seemed that it was his day to go through the infiltration course. Ralph and I were amazed.

"Do even doctors have to hike, shoot and go through all the rest of it?" I asked.

Jimmy snorted.

"Every person in my division has to do it," he stated proudly, "including myself."

"Well," I said, "if you'll excuse us we'll go find the surgeon and have a talk with him."

Jimmy waved us away.

"Whew!" Ralph ran a finger around the inside of his collar. "I'm glad we got out of there before he made us take a twenty-five-mile hike."

"Yeah," I said, "but even that would make more sense than having doctors crawl under the fire of machine guns on an infiltration course."

"Sure," Ralph agreed, "but don't put the blame for that on Jimmy because I happen to know it is a War Department order."

"War Department, my eye," I retorted. "You mean some guy in the Pentagon had a brain storm and published an order without first figuring what the results would be?"

"Brain storm?" The corners of Ralph's mouth quirked. "Why, Cookie! You don't mean to say we've got psychos in the Pentagon, do you?"

"Nuts!" I said. "Let's go see how the surgeon is making out.

For a forty-eight-year-old gentleman who had just crawled about a hundred yards on his belly, keeping barely beneath the cones of fire from half a dozen machine guns, the surgeon was doing all right. We found him watching, with some apprehension, however, the wrigglings of another officer undergoing the same ordeal.

"What's the matter with that officer's hands?" I asked, having noticed that every few yards the man would pause, lift the palms of his hands from the rocky soil, and gaze at them intently.

"Nothing— I hope," replied the surgeon bitterly. "That is one of the finest surgeons in the world and his hands are as sensitive as any great musician's. If he gets injured out there in any way it will, no doubt, cost the lives of thousands of young Americans who will need his skill later on."

"Who was fool enough to subject him to such a risk?" I demanded, hotly.

"You ought to know," the surgeon retorted grimly. "You're from the War Department and, since you brought up the subject, I'd like to tell you that yesterday three young nurses in an evacuation hospital broke their legs while going through the obstacle course. Now, instead of being ready to care for the sick and wounded, they have to be cared for themselves."

"You're kidding," I accused.

"I don't kid about broken legs. They're nothing to laugh off."

"Has anybody else gotten hurt?"

"Our hospital is not exactly empty," said the surgeon dryly. "Take the case of our judge advocate. He is fifty years old, but he had to take his twenty-five-mile hike the same as everybody else. That put him in the hospital with a bad heart, and when I say bad, I mean bad! Can you tell me how marching twenty-five miles in eight hours in any way trains a judge advocate to render proper legal decisions?"

The best I could think of under the circumstances was to say that someone must have misconstrued the meaning of the order, and then to change the subject.

"Have any men been too frightened to go under all those bullets, or jumped up and gotten hit?"

"None of them has gotten hit, so far," the surgeon reached over and tapped three times on a near-by wooden post, "but a few have frozen to the ground and couldn't go through with it."

"What happens to men like that?"

"Usually they have to be carried away in an ambulance."

"Would they be put in the NP ward?" asked Ralph.

"No," said the surgeon, a little surprised by the question, "not unless they failed to recover in a reasonable length of time. What made you bring that up?"

We told the surgeon about the inquiry we were conducting and the imposing number of psychoneurotic cases we had discovered were coming from the division commanded by Jimmy-the-Hard. Immediately the surgeon's attitude changed.

Evidently it had been all right to blame anything so impersonal as the War Department, but any implied criticism of the surgeon's commanding general was something else again. It was easy to see that, as a doctor true to his Hippocratic oath, he would have liked to unburden himself freely, but as a division surgeon loyalty to his immediate commander prevented him from doing so.

The surgeon was on a spot. It didn't look as though we were going to get much more out of him so I suggested to Ralph that we go see some of the regimental doctors, and particularly those who took daily sick calls. But at first we didn't have much luck there either.

Most of the junior medicos were new in the service and rather uncertain regarding military matters. They were confident enough in their medical knowledge but definitely in awe of rank and brass hats. However, we finally ran into one called "Smitty" who had a sense of humor and a fear of no man. In him we struck pay dirt.

"I make a game out of it," he shrugged, when we pinned him down on the subject of psychoneurotics attending sick call.

"What do you mean, a game?"

He gave us a wide grin.

"Well, they say they have it and I say they don't."

"Have what?"

"Why, whatever aches or pains they complain about."

"You mean they don't actually have them?" Ralph asked eagerly.

"Now, don't take me too literally," Smitty hedged. "It depends upon the type of pains they have. There is always the possibility that some organic disorder is present. So, in certain types of cases I don't take a chance, but send them to the hospital for examination."

Smitty seemed like an understanding sort of guy, so I decided to take a chance on my next question.

"Do you ever send them to the hospital when you don't think there are any organic disorders?"

Smitty dragged deeply on a cigarette. He appraised me openly, but without offense or rudeness. Finally he decided upon his answer.

"Yes," he said, "I do."

Now we were getting somewhere!

"Tell us about it, will you? We certainly need all the help we can get."

Smitty cocked his feet on a desk, looked up at the ceiling and then began.

"First, there's the mama's boy. He's scared to death the minute he gets into a uniform and he never gets over it. The men in barracks soon begin to make fun of him and he has no comeback. Then they begin to bully him. The noncoms bawl him out in the hope of arousing some combative spirit in the poor drip, but he doesn't have any. As soon as that becomes known he gets beaten up a couple of times, by kids half his size, and then he begins coming to the infirmary with his nerves all shot to pieces. Well, pretty soon I take pity on the baby and the next time he shows up on sick report I send him to the hospital for a rest or in the hope he may be transferred into another outfit and get a new start."

Smitty's glance came down from the ceiling to see if he was boring us. I guess the urgency in our eyes reassured him because he began again without prompting.

"Then there's the awkward, simple kind of a guy that hardly stays in one outfit long enough to hang up his pack. The boys don't pick on him because he can take care of himself in a physical way and he's too dumb to be kidded. But the poor devil can't remember left from right, and on the target range he couldn't hit a bull on the stern with a bass fiddle. Well, he's juggled around like a hot potato, from one place to another, under all sorts of pretexts, for a lot of different jobs, and he can't do any of them. Eventually the idea finally penetrates that nobody wants him and that he is different from other people— on both of which counts he is more or less correct—so he gets fed up, feels sick and thinks a hospital might not be a bad place to try.

"Well, what the heck!" Smitty's hands turned palms up. "It's about the only place he hasn't been so I give him a chance at that." Again Smitty's glance lowered and one hand squeezed across his pursed lips while he regarded us with a comical air.

"Of course, I don't want you to think I'm passing the buck, but the main thing is, I've got a lot of friends in the regiment. They've all got some men that keep their companies in hot water with their battalion commander, the regimental commander and sometimes even the division commander. So the officers are always after me, saying, 'Smitty, give us a break.' 'Smitty, you gotta help the outfit,' and 'Smitty, all the other guys are doing it,' and so on and so forth until finally it's what the heck again. After all, this is my regiment as well as theirs, and I have to live with my friends."

It was hard for Ralph and me to find fault with Smitty on that score. After all, the members of a regiment, and particularly one soon going into battle, had to stick together. But I wondered whether or not Smitty's regiment was the only one getting away with something, or if the others in the division were doing the same thing. So I asked him, pointblank.

"At first," he replied, "we all tried to talk the boys out of thinking they had backaches and pains. When that didn't do any good, some of us thought they might be discouraged if we gave them a big dose of salts, or something like that whenever they showed up at sick call."

Smitty stopped talking and just sat there, looking at us.

"Did the salts do any good?" Ralph ventured finally.

"If you mean, did it help keep the complainers away from the infirmary, yes." Smitty lowered his feet and leaned forward. His eyes turned hard, with no trace of humor left in them. "But if you mean, did it make them any better rifle shots, or better able to march or drill, or be better soldiers, the answer is 'no'."

Ralph shifted uneasily in his chair and I knew he thought it would be unfair to ask Smitty any more questions along those particular lines. I felt the same way, so I tried something else.

"Doctor," I said, "the psychiatrists at induction stations have been rejecting about fifteen per cent of all the men called. Now, it seems that a division like this gets rid of some seven per cent more as ineffectuals. Where do they go?"

"Some get discharged and some go to the Army Service Forces."

"And would you take that to mean that from fifteen to twenty out of every one hundred Americans are psychoneurotics?"

The tension went out of Smitty's face and he lit a cigarette before replying.

"I'm not a psychiatrist, but in my opinion we are all potential psychoneurotics."

Ralph nearly fell out of his chair.

"I knew that one was coming, Cookie!" he laughed, and then went on to quote, " 'Everybody's crazy but me and thee, and sometimes I think that even thee is a little crazy'."

"No, that's not it," Smitty was also smiling. "It's what is known as a threshold or breaking point. Some are pushed beyond it when they are still children, others when they first get out into the world or into strange, new surroundings, and still others are fortunate enough never to have reached their limit of endurance."

I tried to reason that out, but finally shook my head.

"To me you're just talking about plain, everyday intestinal fortitude."

"Well, call it what you like, but do you believe that everyone has the same amount, under the same conditions and for the same length of time?"

"No, of course not," I looked at Ralph, who indicated his

agreement, "but there must be some way of making soldiers out of those discards, regardless of how much they've got of whatever it is we're talking about."

Smitty looked at me, a little pityingly, I thought.

"Not being much of a soldier myself, I couldn't tell you how to do it," he said, "but as a doctor, I assure you it cannot be accomplished by order, by strong-arm methods, or by dosing with salts."

"Well," I sighed, getting up to leave, "it's nice to know some of the ways it can't be done because if we learn enough of those, we might figure out how it can."

"Yeah," said Ralph glumly, after we had thanked Smitty and bade him goodbye, "if there are any ways left."

Leaving the infirmary in a staff car we traveled past block after block of bleak two-story wooden barracks, each the same as all the others. No grass showed anywhere; just red, sandy clay. Someone had planted small trees along the roadside, but they drooped forlornly, like so many stalks of wilted celery.

Soon we reached the last of the buildings and swung right, where mile after mile of mesquite and cactus stretched as far as the eye could carry, meeting the distant shadows of an early sundown.

"There's the obstacle course," Ralph pointed out.

We both gazed at that breaker of nurses' legs; at the rows of hurdles, mazes of barbed wire, large concrete pipes and the wooden wall through and over which every single member of Jimmy-the-Hard's division had to struggle before being acknowledged a soldier. And even as we looked, first one and then a half dozen other figures in fatigue clothes popped suddenly out of the concrete pipes, dashed madly at the wooden wall and came clattering over, laughing and shouting.

"Stop the car," I directed the driver.

Ralph and I got out and walked toward the small party of soldiers who were assembling near the wall. They watched our approach with some apprehension and a certain amount of guarded alertness. Any time an enlisted man sees an officer coming straight toward him, he takes it for granted it is for some ulterior and disagreeable purpose.

The smallest member of the group stepped forward to render a salute. He had wide-open blue eyes, a freckled snub nose, and stood not more than five feet four, but he wore the chevrons of a corporal on his sleeve.

"How old are you, Corporal?" I asked, as an opener to the conversation.

"Eighteen, sir," he snapped it out so glibly I knew he was accustomed to answering that question.

Obviously the boy was lying. If he ever shaved it was for exercise alone, yet he stood there firm as a rock, ready to argue me down if I tried to make anything out of it. But I had something else on my mind.

"Who ordered you to go through the obstacle course just now?"

A look of surprise came over the faces of the whole group.

"No one told us to," the corporal seemed a little embarrassed. "We just did it ourselves," and the others nodded their agreement. "We've been on fatigue all day unloading trucks, so we thought we'd have a little fun on the way to barracks."

It was Ralph's and my turn to be surprised. Going through all that exertion after a hard day's work was not our idea of amusement. However, we were satisfied no unjust requirements had been demanded of these soldiers.

"How do you like this division?" I asked next.

The corporal's chest inflated to a point that almost lifted him off his toes.

"It's the best da-- the best division in the Army," he stated truculently, and the men behind him moved forward a step in case there was any argument about that.

Ralph was not only amused but very much taken with the kid's spirit.

"How about the psychoneurotics?" he demanded suddenly.

The corporal's eyes blinked and some of his assurance departed. For the first time he glanced over his shoulder, seeking the support of his friends.

"He means chemical warfare," suggested a tall youth with curly blond hair.

"Oh," the corporal was himself again. "One of them new poison gases! No sir, we ain't had no instruction in that, yet."

Ralph and I had a hard time keeping our faces straight.

"It's not a gas," Ralph explained. "It's a disease. Men get it because they are in the Army and want to get out. They say they are sick and ride the sick report until they get in a hospital. And they keep on doing that until they are discharged."

The corporal opened his mouth and then shut it again without speaking. He had suddenly realized that the question related to enlisted men and one enlisted man doesn't take sides with officers against other enlisted men. Over each countenance in the group there began to appear that stolid look assumed by all soldiers when they are about to deny any knowledge of what an officer is talking about.

"General Marshall is the one who wants to know," I said, hastily.

I had seen it happen before. The average GI puts little trust in the motives of strange officers, but The Chief not only commands the soldiers, he also bosses the officers, so he isn't exactly an officer himself; he's better than that. In fact, he is the Number One guy. At the mention of his name most GIs are willing to talk, and the corporal was no exception.

"We do get some of them fellows once in a while," he admitted.

The corporal lowered his eyes and began to make marks with the toe of one shoe. His friends also looked away, as though not wishing to intrude on a delicate conversation.

"What do you think about them?" I asked. "Do you suppose they are really sick or could you make soldiers out of them?"

The corporal frowned, in youthful concentration.

"Naw," he stated emphatically. "You couldn't make soldiers out of them guys."

"Why not?"

The corporal looked off at the distant horizon as though the answer was somewhere out across all those miles of mesquite. Finally it seemed to come to him.

"I guess it's because it wouldn't be worth the trouble. I mean, you wouldn't have anything when you got through. Them kind of guys are always bitching and trying to bellyache their way out of doing things, but mostly they just don't want to be soldiers."

"Do you?" I asked quickly.

"Sure," he shot right back, "as long as there's a war on."

"Then do you think it is fair that you have to go fight when they don't?"

"I wouldn't know if it's fair," the corporal was trying hard to give an honest answer, "but I don't know what can be done about it. I don't want any of that kind around me in a fight."

"That's right, Shorty," spoke up the curly-headed lad. "We

got enough lookin' out for ourselves without playin' nursemaid to any crybabies."

And that's all they had to say.

So, wishing them good luck, Ralph and I returned to our car. As we climbed in the distant beat of a bass drum throbbing in martial cadence came to our ears.

"Sunset parade," said Ralph. "Let's go see it."

We arrived just as Jimmy-the-Hard turned out to take his place at the reviewing stand. Then came rank after rank of soldiers, every man in step, every helmet in line. Bayonets glittered, flags whipped in the breeze and salutes came with snap and precision.

"It is a damn fine division, Cookie," declared Ralph, thrilled as everyone might be at such a sight.

"Sure it is," I conceded, "and no wonder, with all the eight balls thrown out."

"But it's worth it. Just look at those boys go by! What's a thousand men compared to having an outfit like that?"

"Listen, Ralph," I got ready to pour cold water on his enthusiasm, "how many divisions are there in the Army?"

He turned reluctantly from viewing the parade.

"About a hundred, I guess. Why?"

"Well, you can bet that if Jimmy-the-Hard has been using the Medical Corps to get rid of his psychoneurotics, the other division commanders have caught on and are doing the same thing. With a hundred two-star generals working at it, how many guys do you think have had the skids put under them?"

"OK, I can count," said Ralph, "but what's the difference? Most of them probably end up in the Service Forces."

"Maybe," I retorted, "and maybe not. I'm thinking about what the corporal told us. Remember? A guy who is nervous in the service just doesn't want to be a soldier, and no matter where a person is in the Army, he is still a soldier."

"You mean we've got to go to the Service Forces and see what has happened to all those discards?" Ralph asked sadly.

I merely nodded my head.

"All right," Ralph took one last fond look at the tail end of the parade, "but if I land up in an NP ward myself, I don't want you coming around asking me any questions."

"I won't," I promised, "because I'll probably be in the cot right next to yours."

CHAPTER 3

THE CHICKEN OR THE EGG

~~~~~~

BEFORE THE ARMY WAS REORGANIZED, EARLY IN 1942, all soldiers were expected to do their own chores. But when the Service Forces were established and assigned the task of "housekeeping" for the Ground Forces, things became quite different.

It soon got so that Ground Forces soldiers could hardly be expected to police up around their own barracks. In addition, they began looking down their noses at GIs in the Service Forces, and not infrequently referred to them as "4-Fs," both officers and enlisted men alike.

It is true that a large number of Service Forces personnel were over age or below the required physical standards for field duty, but that did not necessarily mean they were inactive mentally, or didn't know the score. Indeed, I have seen many a one who, in a poker game, could take the haughtiest combat soldier to a cleaning. One such was a colonel of cavalry, known for forty years in the service as "Pappy."

When Ralph Bing and I walked in on Pappy, he was commanding one of the largest camps in the country. His was the task of housing, supplying and furnishing overhead for two divisions in training, as well as for a replacement training center. He seemed to be taking it very much in his stride, although at the time of our arrival he was somewhat wroth at one of the division commanders who had just departed with his division for overseas.

"I didn't mind so much dog-robbing for The Duke," Pappy

said, referring to the division commander in question, "but I don't like having to wash his dirty linen for him."

"What do you mean?" we asked, somewhat surprised.

"Just before he left, the Duke got authority to transfer all his ineffectuals to me, and that's what he did, the ingrate, all 824 of them."

"What are they like?"

"I haven't found out yet," Pappy viciously tamped tobacco into the bowl of a large pipe, "the whole bunch are either in the stockade, AWOL, or in the hospital."

"Are those in the hospital psychoneurotics?" Ralph asked eagerly.

Pappy regarded Ralph over the flame of a match. Ralph and he had been on opposite sides in many a polo game, and knew each other well.

"Since when have you been using four-bit words like that, Ralph," Pappy inquired plaintively, "and what do you care whether they are psycho-what-you-may-call-its or not?"

We explained to Pappy that we were inquiring into the subject of psychoneurosis because the Chief of Staff had so directed. We also told him how far we had progressed, but in doing so, made full use of all the medical terms we had acquired up to that stage of the inquiry. Pappy was good naturedly impressed.

"You're just the fellows I've been looking for," he grinned. "I have a couple of doctors over at the hospital who talk that same kind of language. I'd like to see the four of you together."

Ralph hitched his chair forward.

"Give us a five goal handicap," he offered, "and we'll take 'em on."

"Handicap or no handicap," I interposed, "we will have to get together with them because we want to find out what has become of all the psychoneurotics sent to the hospitals by Ground Forces units. We have been told that the majority of them are eventually assigned to appropriate duties in the Service Forces."

Pappy's comment on the appropriateness of all personnel policies in general and that one in particular, reeked of the stables. When we finally managed to fumigate the atmosphere with assurances of our own non-partisan attitude in the matter, he cooled off sufficiently to ring for his director of personnel.

In response to insistent buzzing, a tall, bespectacled lieutenant colonel appeared, wearing a suppressed smirk of assurance. Evidently he felt quite confident of his familiarity with personnel matters and of his ability to answer any questions our less well informed minds might devise.

"How many psychoneurotics, who originally served in the Ground Forces, have we received from hospitals?" Pappy demanded without any preliminaries whatever.

The lieutenant colonel blinked a couple of times and his jaws worked like a goldfish gulping air, but nothing came out. Finally he had to admit reluctantly that he had no figures on psychoneurotics. In doing so, he even had trouble pronouncing the word.

"Then go see if you can find some," Pappy directed, and the director of personnel made a chagrined exit.

"I don't believe he can get that information without going through the individual records of every man on the post," I said.

Pappy leaned over and tapped sharply on an ash stand to empty the dottle from his pipe.

"Aren't you the optimist?" he jeered, between taps. "Personally, I don't think he could find anything worthwhile if he went through all the records in the Army. I've never seen anything about psychoneurotics on any of the service records I ever looked at, nor any other kind of a remark that would prevent or hinder a man's transfer out of a unit."

"You mean that company commanders are giving satisfactory ratings to men who are not adaptable to the service?"

"Sure, they mark men satisfactory who aren't adaptable to anything. Otherwise the company commanders would have to put their undesirables up before a Section Eight Board and the number they get rid of that way you could put in your eye."

"So the Section Eight Boards are not finding those men as possessing traits and character unsuitable to the service?"

"How can they? The men's ratings are kept up and put on progress charts so as to make a good showing for the organization. Then, when a man comes up before a Board of Officers there isn't enough evidence for the Board to act on. That means the officer who put him before the Board gets called down. So, next time, he either gets the guy transferred or else sent to a hospital."

"Yeah, and it's those men who are sent to hospitals from Ground Forces units that we're interested in. We want to find out how many are returned to duty in the Service Forces." I reached for my hat. "Those two psychiatrists of yours may keep some kind of a record on it."

"Maybe," Pappy replied, "but even if they do, which I doubt very much, you still wouldn't have the whole picture."

"What do you mean?" Ralph inquired.

"Well, let's begin at the time when men are first inducted," Pappy stood up and reached automatically for his riding crop— the identifying badge of old-time field officers. "The Air Forces get seventy-five per cent of all their quotas from men in the upper brackets of the Army's intelligence tests. The Ground and Service Forces get what's left. But, every Ground Forces unit going overseas leaves behind its hospital cases, AWOL's and ineffectuals for us to absorb, so you can see that, in the long run, we are bound to end up with all the men the other two commands don't think they can use."

"Do you use them?" I asked, following Pappy out to the car waiting to take us to another meeting with Army psychiatrists.

"I use anybody I can get, even if they have only one leg. I've got to, or I couldn't operate. My biggest trouble is keeping the men away from those doctors."

"You mean the psychiatrists don't think your men are well enough to do duty, even in the Zone of Interior?"

"Huh!" grunted Pappy. "Just wait 'til you meet those birds."

Our first impression of the doctors in question was not encouraging. The eldest was tall, with a stooped frame on which a captain's uniform hung shapelessly. The other was a short, stocky major, badly in need of a haircut. Neither was over-friendly, nor appeared particularly eager to cooperate.

They did not keep any records of where their patients came from, nor what became of them after leaving the hospital. Such information might be available in the Registrar's Office, but the doctors were not sure. It looked as though we were not going to get much out of the conference when Ralph unexpectedly touched off some oral fireworks.

"Is psychoneurosis hereditary?" he asked, for no apparent reason at all.

"Of course it is!" said the elderly captain hastily.

"Certainly not!" instantly corrected the major.

The captain's lips compressed and his eyes were defiant. The major glowered back from under heavy brows. Behind Ralph's poker-lidded orbs I detected some lurking mischief.

He prompted the major, "Where does psychoneurosis come from?"

He received a prompt answer.

"In ninety-five per cent of our cases, some environmental condition is the basic cause of the disorder," began the major.

"That is debatable," interposed the captain, and got a dirty look for his pains.

"The results of early environment are particularly evidenced in the army," resumed the major. "For twenty years our younger generation has been told and retold that all wars are wrong. In school and at home, the theme has been the same. No wars! No killings! As children they have even been forbidden to play with toy soldiers or guns. Then, they are suddenly inducted into the military service and expected to become soldiers and kill people."

The major gave a contemptuous snort, directed at me, Pappy, and Ralph; the captain being completely ignored.

"One day a child can't even have a miniature tank or airplane for Christmas, and almost the next day he is put into the real thing and told to go out and start shooting at people. In the last few years everyone has seen the government forced to provide for its incompetents. Suddenly, those same ineffectuals are called upon to go out and help take care of the government, at the risk of their lives," the major's hands gesticulated frantically. "Who does the Army think it is to change everything overnight? God?"

Ralph and I sat back and sought desperately for an appropriate answer. Pappy complacently pulled out pipe and tobacco with a sly grin at our discomfiture.

"Wait a minute," Ralph said half angrily, "there are plenty of boys who are not only willing but eager to fight for their country."

The major brushed that aside.

"Granted," he allowed, "but there are also an unfortunate number of men, both young and old, who never have fought for anything and never will."

There was, of course, some truth to that statement.

"Could not wanting to fight produce a neurosis?" I inquired.

"It could," stated the major, "and, peculiarly enough, a desire to fight might just as easily do the same thing."

"That sounds kind of screwy to me," I finally stated. "Perhaps you can explain your ideas to us in words of one syllable."

"It's quite simple," the major expanded, happy under the warmth of our combined attention, "the man who never has wanted to fight and who doesn't care too much how he goes about avoiding any kind of physical conflict is soon eliminated from the Army. Right?"

The major's inquiring look brought nods of understanding and agreement from three of us. The captain remained non-committal.

"But what about the psychoneurotic whose pride forces him to try to be as good a soldier or better than his comrades? Even though he has avoided the stress of conflict all his life, his ego will not permit him to show inferiority in wartime. Therefore, he enters the Army and may even go to battle, not once but several times. Yet, the more he forces himself to become what he would like to be, instead of what he actually is, the more stress he undergoes and the greater will be his neurotic reactions when he finally breaks."

Pappy puffed prodigiously on his pipe while waiting to see how Ralph and I would answer that one.

"It seems to me," I began, "that you are being contradictory. If a man has sufficient pride to force himself into trying to be a good soldier, he certainly must have grown up in a good environment."

The captain leaned forward eagerly, but I motioned him to silence so the major could reply.

"That depends upon what you mean by a good environment. A boy might grow up in a very fine house but still be spoiled by his mother or sisters. He also might be completely dominated or even abused by his father. Or, where there has been a separation or divorce the boy might spend his adolescence with only one parent. There are thousands of cases where the economic surroundings of a person appear normal or even better than average, yet underneath are emotional conditions that have led or are leading to neurotic reactions."

The major leaned back, indicating that he had stated his case, so I turned to the captain.

"In what way do you differ with the major's ideas?"

"I do not disagree with the major except as to the basic cause of psychoneurosis. It has been demonstrated that the majority of cases come from families where conditions are not normal. According to the major's school of thought the surroundings are to blame for the resultant neurotic reactions, but it is my belief that the parents themselves were psychoneurotic, otherwise, those conditions never would have come about."

The major stirred, uneasily, but I frowned him down so the captain could continue.

"The selection of animals for any given purpose is always along definite bloodlines. For racing, you require thoroughbred horses or greyhounds; for hunting, bird dogs; for fighting, game-cocks; and so on. You could no more train a bulldog to hunt quail than you could teach a cat to dive into water and catch fish. Human beings are the same."

"That's just fine," I permitted myself some sarcasm. "If we follow that theory, all we have to do is look through the city directories and telephone books to find men who are in the business of being infantrymen, tank destroyers, paratroopers, ball turret gunners, and so forth. Otherwise, we couldn't get together an Army."

The captain flushed, yet he managed to restrain his emotions.

"Your statement is, of course, somewhat farfetched," he accused, "but not much more so than is the system under which the Army now operates."

"What system are you referring to?" demanded Ralph.

The captain scratched his chin.

"That system whereby any man not afflicted with a bodily defect is considered capable of becoming a combat soldier."

"Well, why shouldn't he be?" Ralph wanted to know.

"Let me answer your question in this manner," said the captain, like a conjurer about to produce a silver dollar from behind the ear of a small boy. "On this side of the room we have a hundred men with no bodily defects, but who are mentally unable to adjust themselves to the Army or to the thoughts of entering combat. On the other side of the room are a hundred men with various bodily defects, but also with a keen sense of duty and a burning desire to fight for their country. Which group would you take?"

Pappy's feet thumped the floor where they had been hooked around the rungs of his chair.

"Bell's hells," he almost shouted. "Even I can answer that

question. Give me the fellows who want to do something and I'll find a job for them!"

"Exactly," crowed the captain, "but the Army insists upon following the opposite procedure.

"Baloney!" Ralph got to his feet. "Out of a thousand able-bodied Americans you might cull out a hundred who wouldn't fight; as likewise out of a thousand cripples you could find a hundred who want to get into the scrap. Just the same, your proposition is a ten to one shot, both ways, and doesn't mean that there is anything wrong with the Army's system of selection."

Before the captain could reply, his companion psychiatrist spoke up.

"The captain only means that the Army's system of selection has, in the past, been based upon standards which have not given sufficient consideration to psychiatric disorders that quite frequently are more serious than physical defects. Such disorders are less easily discerned."

It appeared to me that we were headed toward an unprofitable argument, so I terminated the interview and almost forcibly dragged Ralph and Pappy away from the two psychiatrists.

"Doggone it, Cookie," Ralph grumbled, "you never did let me find out whether psychoneurosis is hereditary or environmental."

"Listen," I almost scolded, "what we really came here to find out about was how many of these psychos get returned to duty."

Ralph's answering silence was broken by Pappy's acrimonious chuckle.

"Heredity or environment?" He savored the words like a gourmet tasting a sauce. "Seems to me like trying to find out which came first, the chicken or the egg."

"Horse feathers!" Ralph flared up. "You can't feel, taste, see or prove a neurosis. It's just one guy's brain tuning in on another's. If the wave length is wrong you get a commercial instead of Buck Rogers. All I wanted to find out was, who is the sponsor?"

"Hold everything," I implored, "what I'm interested in is, where do these psychos end up after they get in a general hospital? Let's go to the registrar's office."

We proceeded without further argument, but before giving us what information was available, the registrar asked us to see the commanding officer. That was all right with us, and particularly so when we found him to be one of the old crowd from Fort Benning, where we had all been stationed together in pre-war days.

"Bob!" I shouted, at sight of him.

He practically leaped across his desk to greet us.

"Ralph! Cookie!" He embraced the two of us and then looked quizzically at Pappy. "Don't tell me you three have been swinging polo mallets at each other and need medical attention."

"Not quite," I answered, as we all took seats and made ourselves comfortable. Then I told him of our problem.

Instantly he became serious.

"You certainly picked yourselves a hot subject." Bob soberly reached into his desk drawer and drew out a paper.

"I've been keeping a record on psychiatric cases since I came here. This will probably give you the figures you are looking for."

He adjusted his bifocals and began to read from the paper.

"Out of more than three thousand cases entering this hospital, we have returned about seven hundred to duty. Ten have been turned over to the Veterans Administration, five have been released to the custody of their parents, and about two hundred have been sent to other hospitals for specialized treatment."

Bob paused impressively and I could see Ralph doing some rapid finger calculations.

"Go on," he looked up at Bob, "how about the other two-thirds?"

Bob carefully placed his reference paper in the exact center of his desk. He bore down on its edges with the palms of his hands, in emphasis of what he was about to tell us.

"The other two thousand," he said slowly, "have been discharged for physical disability."

"Any of them battle casualties?" I asked, in amazement.

"About twenty per cent have had overseas service, but less than half of that number have been in combat of any sort."

We sat silently digesting that piece of information for several minutes. Eventually Ralph sighed resignedly and turned to me.

"That means that about fifteen hundred men from this one hospital have been given a disability discharge simply because they could not adjust themselves to the Army. And this hospital is only one of a hundred others."

"Yes," I agreed, "and it also means that out of every thirty psychoneurotics who go into a hospital, not more than seven ever return to duty."

"But even so, what happened to those seven hundred men?" Pappy scrubbed puzzledly on his head with the palms of both hands. "I know I didn't get them."

"I'm afraid you did, Pappy," Bob contradicted, "only you probably didn't keep them."

"What do you mean, I didn't keep them?" Pappy was belligerent. "Do you think I transferred them out of my command?"

"Not exactly," Bob smiled ruefully. "What I think really happened was that most of them got back into the hospital again."

"Oh!" The exclamation came from all three of us. I finally asked the obvious question.

"What you're saying is that the records show a certain number of psychiatric patients as being returned to duty, but actually they are still psychoneurotics and get themselves back onto sick report as soon as possible, probably in the hope of obtaining a disability discharge. Is that correct?"

"That," Bob assured me solemnly, "is just what I think is happening."

Again we lapsed into silence while considering the implications of Bob's disclosures. It was a disqueting thought, that otherwise able-bodied individuals were mentally capable of rendering themselves not only unable to serve their country but as actually qualifying for disability benefits because of their inability to become soldiers.

"We never had any troubles like this before the war," Ralph complained, sliding the sole of one shoe back and forth along a crack in the floor. "How did it start, and where did all these psychiatrists suddenly come from?"

Bob picked up his reference papers and carefully replaced them in the desk drawer.

"It is quite a story," he stated. "At the beginning, we brought in about five hundred psychiatrists, the majority of whom came from state institutions for the feeble-minded. Just recently, in order to increase the number of psychiatrists the Air Forces have started special courses at some of their psychiatric centers, where regular medical officers may go for 'on the job training' so they can act as psychiatrists. Now, the Surgeon General is going to establish similar courses in some of the Service Forces hospitals."

I was somewhat puzzled.

"Aren't there special psychiatric medical schools where they could be sent?"

"No," Bob answered, "there are only the special courses in psychology and psychiatry which are given to a greater or lesser degree in all medical schools."

"Then a psychiatrist is just a regular doctor who practices psychiatry?" Ralph queried.

"Oh no," Bob corrected. "Of course, any registered doctor could legally practice psychiatry, but he would not be accepted as a psychiatrist by the medical profession nor by the American Psychiatric Association until he had completed a certain amount of extra studies and also finished his training for a given period of time under a recognized psychiatrist."

"And now the Army is beginning to give what might be called, 'Get-rich-quick courses' in psychiatry?"

"That's right."

I turned and looked significantly at Ralph, who mockingly raised an elbow, as though to ward off my obvious intentions.

"I know," he said sadly, before I could get out a word, "you want us to go to school and learn to be psychiatrists."

"Wonderful," Pappy cried gleefully. "That will teach you to go 'round asking whether psychoneurosis is hereditary or environmental."

Ralph gave him a baleful look, but before those two could become embroiled in personalities, we prepared to leave. After all, we had gotten the figures we had come for, depressing as they were. Both Bob and Pappy accompanied us to our car and stood watching as we climbed inside.

"Don't forget, Ralph," Pappy called as the door closed, "be sure and let me know which came first, the chicken or the egg."

Ralph leaned his head out the window.

"I don't know about that," he shouted as we started to move, "but I can tell you right now which end of the horse came first, as far as you're concerned."

Pappy made a face and, as the car pulled away, he and Ralph exchanged salutes. But they were not good salutes, because the thumb of each raised hand rested a bit too near its owner's nose to be accepted as a bona-fide military salutation.

Chapter 4

White Magic

~~~~~~

Wartime travel was always a game of chance, in which some persons were lucky enough to sleep lying down instead of sitting up or not sleeping at all. But those who journeyed with the Army Air Forces were just lucky. Particularly if they were VIPs (very important people) as the radio code described Ralph Bing and me just before our plane swooped down out of a Florida sky of cobalt blue onto the concrete landing strip at Tampa.

Even before the drone of engines was gone from our ears, we were "meeted and greeted" and dispatched on our way in a high-powered limousine to the big convalescent hospital.

Usually, when the Army takes over a hospital, it is some well established medical center, bleak in appearance and purely institutional in type. Not so, however, the Army Air Forces. Their method was to seek out the finest hotels in the most lavish surroundings, to evict the occupants therefrom and convert the luxurious appointments into hospital accommodations for sick, wounded and weary flyers.

This particular hospital stood beside a placid lagoon of vari-colored waters which shimmered on one side while waves from the Gulf of Mexico washed against a long sandy beach on the other. Rows of royal palms rustled a stately welcome as our car swept into the driveway and halted before this center of Air Forces psychiatry.

Ralph and I entered its portals with no little feeling of apprehension and awe. Strange tales had been told us about certain treatments carried on within those walls, procedures almost bordering upon the supernatural or white magic. Consequently, we gazed about curiously as we were escorted through a large rotunda crowded with stalwart young men, all wearing patches of the Army Air Forces. Many of them had from one to two rows of campaign ribbons or decorations.

But it was neither their patches nor decorations that made them distinctive. It was the expression or, rather, the lack of expression on their faces which drew attention. They did not appear dull, vacant-eyed or even reserved. Instead, it was more as if they were completely preoccupied and oblivious of their immediate surroundings. Even though, in many instances, an attractive young woman, obviously a wife, hung in thoughtful attendance at the soldier's side.

For a short while during our progress through the luxurious surroundings of that converted hotel I was completely baffled by the detached bearing of those young men. Then, just as we were being ushered into the chief medical officer's place of business, my mind reached back in recollection of similar individuals I had seen in World War I—and the answer suddenly came to me. Theirs was the preoccupied look of men who had escaped physically, but not mentally, from the mortal dangers to which they had been subjected.

Then came our meeting and introductions to the colonel commanding the hospital and his principal assistant. Just at that moment, an eager young adjutant thrust a telegram at me which, being too busy at the moment to read, I stuffed into my pocket.

We knew the colonel who greeted us to be a pioneer of psychiatry in the Army Air Forces. Also, that his chief assistant was a young major just back from overseas and the author of a new book describing the causes of psychoneurosis in combat areas. We knew, too, that he was an ardent advocate of those ventures into the subconscious, about which we had heard strange rumors.

The colonel and major, also, apparently had heard about Ralph and me because the colonel came directly to the point.

"You are here, I understand, to make inquiry into our methods of treating psychoneurosis."

"Well, not exactly," I temporized. "We understood you were starting a course of instruction in psychiatry for general medical officers and we hoped to get some idea as to its scope and purpose."

"Frankly," he said, "our first objective is to establish the recognition of psychoneurosis as a definite medical disorder requiring special definitive treatment."

Ralph and I edged a little closer together, like a couple of rookies in the big leagues seeking mutual support.

"Does that mean the average medical officer is unwilling to accept the theory of psychiatry?" I ventured.

The colonel smiled a trifle sadly.

"Your average medical officer," he stated, "is, of course, considerably influenced by the opinions of the commander on whose staff he serves. So, when that commander states emphatically that psychoneurosis is just another word for cowardice or lack of intestinal fortitude, his flight surgeon or medical officer is scarcely in a position to diagnose or administer treatment to psychoneurotics."

"Has that been the attitude of the majority of commanders in the air forces?" inquired Ralph.

The colonel toyed thoughtfully with a steel paper cutter before answering.

"I think I could truthfully say that, at first, such was the opinion of all commanders," he said.

"And are they now changing those opinions?" I asked.

The colonel's head bent a little lower over the paper cutter in his hands.

"I wouldn't go so far as to say that they have changed their opinions." The paper cutter bent almost double in the colonel's fingers. "But circumstances have practically forced them to change their attitudes."

Ralph and I waited that one out.

"Take for example, the case of a young captain by the name of O'Brion, who commanded one of our ground units. He was considered one of the best non-rated officers in the Air Forces. Well, he took his outfit on a long conditioning march and one of his lads, whom I will call Smith, fell by the wayside, saying he was too sick to go on."

Ralph and I exchanged grins. We had been confronted with that same problem ourselves.

"Captain O'Brion sent for an ambulance and Smith was hauled off to a hospital. Right after the hike, O'Brion went to see how Smith was getting along and the doctors told him they couldn't find anything the matter with Smith."

Ralph and I grinned again. We'd had that happen to us too.

"Shortly after that O'Brion took his men on another march and again Smith fell out, declaring he was too sick to go on."

"Sure," Ralph agreed. "He got away with it once, so he figured he could keep right on fooling them."

Smith "got away with it" the second time also, but by then the story had gotten around and Captain O'Brion felt that his leadership was being tested and his authority challenged. So, a third time he set out on the road with his unit. It was cold and rainy and Smith didn't go far before getting sick. That time, however, he just laughed at Smith and told him he could be there until the war was over or until he was well enough to walk back to camp.

"Good!" Ralph slapped his knee. "I'll bet that cured him."

The expression on the colonel's face showed plainly that Ralph had jumped to the wrong conclusion, so I asked, "What did happen to Smith?"

The paper cutter in the colonel's hand straightened with a sharp twang.

"Smith died!"

"Died?" Ralph and I were startled into exclaiming. "What did he die of?"

"He contracted pneumonia, presumably from lying on the wet ground. At any rate, some civilians came along in a car, picked him up from alongside the road and carried him to a hospital. On the way, Smith told them how badly he had been treated by Captain O'Brion. One of the civilians was quite sympathetic and returned a few days later to see how Smith was getting along. Unfortunately he was dead. The horrified civilian immediately wrote to some very high public officials regarding the brutal manner in which a private soldier had been treated by an officer."

"Oh, oh!" Ralph said uncomfortably. "That was bad."

"It turned out badly for O'Brion," the colonel acknowledged, "because he was court-martialed and probably will lose his commission."

Ralph and I spent a moment in silent sympathy for O'Brion. Then I asked, "Did that one isolated case change the attitude of those commanders you were talking about?"

"No, but it focused their attention on other incidents and eventually aroused some doubts regarding the reasons for certain very unfortunate accidents. Finally, it was conceded that, whether anyone liked it or not, there was such a thing as psychoneurosis, particularly in the Air Forces."

"Do you mean it is a greater problem in the Air Forces than in the other services?" Ralph asked, somewhat suspiciously.

"Not a greater problem perhaps, but of greater importance, the colonel amended.

"Why?" I asked bluntly.

"Because anxiety frequently develops merely as a result of being in an airplane and quite frequently men can be saved from further disorders if they are removed from flying status in time. Furthermore, if such persons are not discovered, certain disorders may develop so quickly as to be dangerous and sometimes even fatal to other crew members on the same aircraft. For those reasons we believe that prompt diagnoses and early preventive therapy are more important in the Air Forces than in other arms of service."

The colonel's reasoning made sense to me and I could see that Ralph was also impressed. However, there remained certain rumors and stories regarding the therapy or treatment he had referred to, about which Ralph and I were curious. So, somewhat awkwardly perhaps, I broached that subject.

"If the Air Forces has psychiatric conditions peculiar to itself, does it mean your methods of treatment are also different from the other services?"

For a moment, the colonel looked at me intently and then, with a smile, turned to his chief assistant.

"That's in your department, Jim," he said.

Jim accepted the burden of answering my question without the slightest hesitation.

"You undoubtedly are referring to our use of sodium pentothal," he said.

"I don't know the proper name for it," I admitted, "but I've heard several people speak of it as 'truth serum'."

Both doctors smiled.

"It is a hypnotic drug which, when administered intravenously, produces a narcosis," explained Jim.

Ralph and I exchanged rueful glances. We were getting accustomed to being stumped by medical terms but we still felt a little embarrassed over displaying our ignorance, even though our job called for it.

"If I understand this business," I said, wanting to make sure, "you hypnotize a man with a shot in the arm and then ask him questions. Is that right?"

"More or less," Jim admitted. "Usually, when a narcosis has been established—that is, when a patient is in a hypnotic state —he is told that he is in an airplane, or even in combat. By questions, prompting and suggestions, we seek to have him imagine he is again undergoing the conditions of stress which brought about his anxiety state."

"Is that done just to get information, or is it part of a treatment?"

"Both. Primarily, of course, it is a quick means of establishing what is called 'free association'."

Jim paused inquiringly, but my mind immediately leaped back to Bill Shambora and his explanation regarding the "coucher" method of treatment. Evidently the use of pentothal was just a new version of that procedure, so I was glad to indicate my understanding of free association.

Satisfied that I was following him Jim resumed, "Usually, a patient experiences considerable relief after having unburdened himself, even though under the influence of a hypnotic. However, the greatest advantage in the use of pentothal is that often the actual reason or cause for the patient's neurosis becomes definitely established and, consequently, the psychiatrist can better prescribe the proper treatment."

Ralph scratched his head and then looked up with one of his customary grins.

"By that method," he said, "a doctor could also tell whether a man was really psychoneurotic or was just pretending, couldn't he?"

A pained expression appeared on the countenance of the colonel, but it was Jim who retorted quickly, "No *doctor* would need the assistance of pentothal to determine the existence of a neurosis in the type of cases we receive. In fact, I don't even believe it would require a doctor, and if you have any doubts, just come up to the ward and interview some of our patients yourself."

Before Ralph could answer, I intervened.

"We will be glad to do that, but first, I would like to ask about another kind of treatment we have heard mentioned. Something to do with electricity."

Jim glanced at the colonel and received tacit consent to answer the question. "There is a new treatment having to do with electricity. A treatment known as the 'electric shock.' But that is only for psychotics."

"Psychotics?" I puzzled. "Are they any different from psychoneurotics?"

"Considerably," Jim smiled wryly. "The psychotic is of the locked-ward type, the more or less insane person, as compared to the neurotic, or open-ward case."

"But why a distinction in the treatment?" I queried, feeling a little over my depth.

"Actually," the colonel admitted, "the electro-shock treat-

nent is not much beyond the exploration stage. But it has been
used with almost startling success in cases of very severe depression. That is to say, with patients whose disorders are more
mental than nervous."

"How does it operate?" I persisted, with something like morbid fascination.

"An electrode is placed on each side of the patient's brain
and then an electric current is passed from one to the other for
periods of about one-tenth of a second."

A surreptitious glance at Ralph revealed his jaws falling
open like the front of an LCT. Suddenly they snapped shut
again and he threw back his head to laugh.

"What's so funny?" I demanded.

"I just thought of a poem written by Robert W. Service.
Remember? 'I killed the galoot, when he started to shoot
electricity into my walls.' Only in his case, the electricity drove
him nuts."

Jim was not pleased, but the colonel grinned in rueful
appreciation.

"The treatment may sound strange," he admitted, "but it has
been of great benefit to about ninety per cent of our mental
patients."

"But how do they like that kind of treatment?" I asked.

"As a matter of fact," replied Jim, "it is not uncommon for
them to come and ask to have it repeated."

"No wonder they're nuts," I thought, but seeing that Ralph
had the same idea and was about to express it in the form of a
quip, I hastily got to my feet.

"Let's go up to the wards and take a look at some of the cases
you have given those treatments to."

Jim was eager but the colonel, with a deprecatory gesture at his heaped "IN" basket, begged to be excused. Ralph and I thanked him for his help and started off, when the eager young adjutant apologetically blocked our departure.

"Excuse me, sir," he almost blushed, "but I think that telegram I gave you is important. It is from the Chief of Staff."

I remembered the message I had so unceremoniously stuffed into my pocket and hastily pulled it out. It was indeed from the Chief's office, and stated that much publicity was being given to the number of All-American football players classified as 4-F. But the Chief seemed mostly concerned over one player in particular; a top-flight full-back, best known to the trade as "Cannon Ball." The "Ball,'" although recently discharged from the Army on a Certificate of Disability, was now playing professionally in a big way. Those two facts didn't make sense to the Chief and his message directed that Ralph and I look into the matter at once, if we had not already done so.

"What's the matter?" Ralph asked, seeing the expression on my face.

"Nothing much," I replied, "only we should have been yesterday where we can't get to until tomorrow."

"Let's get started, then," said my very cheery and undaunted companion, "maybe we can catch up."

"No," I decided, seeing Jim's quick look of disappointment, "the Cannon Ball can wait. Right now we're going to see some of these boys who have had the pentothal treatment."

The first patient interviewed, however, had not yet been in consultation while under the influence of pentothal. He was a slender, sandy-haired sergeant, just back from a small island base in the Pacific. He stuttered so badly it was extremely difficult to understand what he had to say. Also, most of it was monotonously repetitious with references to the "goddamn

Army" and all of its "chicken manure" procedures. The sergeant definitely was finished, through, fed up! To hell with the whole works—including us, if we wanted to do anything about it.

Through patient questioning and agonizing periods of listening, we finally extracted and pieced together his reasons for that attitude.

He had been in a good outfit, shipped to the Pacific for the purpose of building an air base. Their commanding officer was a regular guy, at first. He and the sergeant got along fine. But it was lonely; no women, nothing to drink and pretty soon the sergeant wasn't getting along with his commanding officer as well as before. The CO seemed to be riding all the Joes. Built himself a loudspeaker on his car and rode around the island, bawling them out for the least little thing. The sergeant got to hating the CO and was in deadly fear of being singled out for a public reprimand over the loud speaker. He would hide whenever he saw the CO's car coming and he felt sure the CO was always tracking him down.

One day he left his tent with nothing on but a pair of shorts and the CO caught him! He was made to stand at attention while the whole island heard him being told off!

The sergeant tried to tell his CO that he was only going down to the beach for a swim but, to his horror, he began to stutter—something he had never done before in his life. The CO thought he was being kidded and bawled the sergeant out worse than ever. The whole island heard and got a laugh!

But, from then on, the sergeant's stuttering got worse, until finally he could hardly talk at all. So now he was home in a hospital and if anyone thought he'd ever go back again they were crazy.

"Jeepers!" said Ralph when the interview was ended and the patient gone. "I'm a worse wreck than the sergeant. Will he ever get over that stuttering?"

Jim shrugged. "Perhaps, but not for a long time."

"Listen," I begged, "how about giving us your psychiatric interpretation of that case?"

"Well, in my opinion, the sergeant's trouble was based upon a latent over-fondness for his commanding officer."

"What?" I puzzled, wondering if I had heard correctly. "Are you implying that the man is a homosexual?"

"It could be so construed." Then Jim smiled. "You'll probably be surprised when I tell you that all men have a certain amount of latent homosexuality in their make-up. If they didn't there would be no close friendships among them and they would be over-sexed in the opposite direction."

Ralph and I exchanged doubtful grins.

"The sergeant we just saw," Jim continued, "had a very warm affection for his commanding officer. While they were in this country and the sergeant had associations with women, his emotions and reactions remained normal. But, on an isolated island far from home, without feminine contacts, his affections centered on the one person he admired and thought the most of. When that person failed to show any return of those feelings, the sergeant was upset. Then, when the object of his affections actually reprimanded him in public, the sergeant's sentiments turned to hatred."

"But why the stutter?" I asked.

"Because the man couldn't express himself. He's boiling inside with emotions he doesn't understand. He would never admit, even to himself, what his real subconscious feelings were regarding his commanding officer."

"And what's going to be the final result?" Ralph inquired.

"The sergeant probably will always hate that particular officer, and, because of him all other officers. Also, since officers, to him, represent the military, he naturally hates the whole military establishment, just as he told you."

"I wonder how many psychoneurotics I'm responsible for," Ralph pondered.

"Not very many, I should judge," Jim said. "But poor leadership and inexperienced officers are responsible for a large percentage of our troubles."

"Well," I said, "let's see another case. But don't bring in any more stutterers because I don't think I can take it."

"I won't," promised Jim, getting up to open the door.

At his signal a tall, towheaded youngster was ushered into the room. His eyes wandered about vaguely, almost unseeingly. Jim had to lead him to a chair.

"What's the matter with you, soldier?" I asked.

The boy's eyes barely focused on my face for a moment and then wandered off into the distance again.

"There isn't anything the matter with me, sir," he replied gently.

"Then why are you here?"

His glance just skimmed the top of my head.

"I don't know why I'm here."

I looked at Ralph, who indicated his own puzzlement.

"Are they treating you all right?" I ventured.

"Oh yes, sir. I'm doing fine." He sat docilely, gazing out through the wall of the hospital, through space, into infinity.

I was stumped and again turned to Ralph but he shook his head. Jim touched the boy's arm, helped him to his feet and guided him to the door.

"What the hell?" I asked, when the door was closed.

Jim silently walked over, sorted some folders on his desk and handed one of them to me. With Ralph looking over my shoulder I read about the boy we had just seen.

Wilbur A. Nostrum, the dossier stated, had been a waist-gunner in a B-17. On its last mission the plane had encountered heavy flak and caught on fire. Wilbur bailed out on his own initiative, catching a glimpse of the B-17 diving into a cloud with a patch of smoke trailing behind. He never saw it or any other member of the crew again. Wilbur was rescued but from then on he was constantly wandering away from his base. When questioned, he was unable to explain where he was going or what he was looking for. Finally, after repeated absences he was sent to a hospital and eventually returned through medical channels to the United States.

"What were his reactions under pentothal?" I queried.

"He blamed himself for bailing out before the other crew members, and for doing it without orders. He feels that he 'ran out' on his buddies and is full of remorse. He can't face the fact that they are gone and he keeps hoping to find them."

"Will he ever recover and be normal again?"

"He will recover from the shock and stress of that particular experience, but I cannot say he will be what you call normal because, in my opinion, he never would be in his present condition if he had been completely normal to begin with."

"Say," Ralph suddenly had a bright idea, "how would it be if we sat in on one of those pentothal interviews?"

Jim was first surprised and then embarrassed.

"Of course, under your directive, you, no doubt, have the authority to be present at such an interview, but I would prefer that you first submit a formal request to my CO."

"Do you mean that our presence would not be considered ethical?"

"I believe it would be deemed most unethical by many psychiatrists. You see, we look upon the confidences of our patients very much as a priest regards confessions, or as a lawyer accepts privileged communications."

I could see that, all right, and decided not to get ourselves involved. So we continued our interviews without going any further into the matter of pentothal.

Each case had a different history but they all followed one general pattern. None of them wanted ever to go back to the place or duties responsible for their breakdown. If returned to duty at all, they wanted to be in a different theater or on a different type airplane. The bomber pilots particularly were anxious to become fighter pilots so as to avoid having the responsibility of other crew members' lives constantly on their minds.

Jim was rather skeptical regarding their ability to return to combat in any capacity.

"In my interviews, they have all shown a pronounced and increasing anxiety over each mission flown, leading up to the one in which their disorders became acute."

"So you believe there would be a recurrence if they went on another mission?"

"That's right."

I thought that over for a moment before another idea occurred to me. "Then you can't really cure them of their neuroses?"

Jim stood up, looked out the window and then turned to face me. "It depends upon what you mean by a cure. In nearly all cases we can effect a certain degree of recovery. We can remove the tension and depression but we still do not consider them entirely well."

I looked hopefully at Ralph for further inspiration but he glumly shook his head. The farther we advanced into the realm of psychiatry, the more difficult became the answers.

"It seems to me," I summarized, "that you can rehabilitate these people to the extent of their being able to carry on, either in civil life or on non-combatant duties, but you can't fix them up to where they can go back and fight. Is that correct?"

Jim looked down thoughtfully at the case histories of the men we had been interviewing. "I don't believe I could answer that question."

"Well," I sighed, turning to Ralph, "let's get going. At least we've learned something new about the treatment of psycho-neurotics."

Somewhat disconsolately, Ralph shook hands with Jim and followed me down to the car. The royal palms seemed to bow us off along the highway.

"Do you know, Cookie," Ralph settled back wearily, "maybe this stuff is getting me down. I'm not feeling so well myself."

"Let me see your hands," I said casually.

He extended them listlessly and I turned them over, as a psychiatrist would do, to see if the palms were sweaty. Realizing the implication, Ralph snatched them back again.

"Maybe you need a shot of pentothal, Ralphie," I grinned.

"No more than you do," said Ralph, as he looked at me with an intent, examining gaze.

CHAPTER 5

DOUBLE OR NOTHING

~~~~~~

WHEN, IN 1943, IT WAS FOUND THAT FOURTEEN MEM-
bers of the Rice University football team had been rejected for
military service, the public was somewhat surprised. But, when
Tulsa's undefeated team journeyed to the Sugar Bowl with
twenty-four of its members in the 4-F class, that surprise turned
to caustic criticism. Then, to make matters worse, a one-time
All-American, just discharged for physical disability, began playing professional football right in the War Department's own
home town.

"So what?" Ralph Bing grumbled while he and I were on
our way to interview this man. "What's The Cannon Ball and
his playing professional ball got to do with our study on psychoneurotics?"

"Look," I replied, pulling out a list furnished by our home
office. "Here are the names of about two dozen big-leaguers of
one sort or another, all rejected or discharged from the Army
for physical disability. From what we've seen so far, at least
a third of 'em are bound to be psychos."

"Huh!" Ralph grunted. "If there's any neurosis connected
with The Cannon Ball, I bet it's on the part of those guys who
try to stop him when he's totin' the pigskin."

"Totin' the pigskin and carrying a sixty-pound pack are two
different things," I pointed out. "Let's wait until we see the guy
and find out how come he can do the one but not the other."

Ralph agreed to withhold judgment until we had seen The
Ball. We found him in a neat little cottage earned and paid for,
no doubt, by his ability to proceed five yards at a time against

71

violent opposition. He received us graciously and even offered to fix a drink, which Ralph and I did not refuse.

Once we were all comfortable and feeling no particular pain, he came right to the point. "I take it you came here to find out how I could be discharged from the Army for a physical disability and still be able to play professional football. Is that correct?"

We admitted that that was the reason for our visit.

"Well," he resumed, looking pointedly at the signet ring on Ralph's left hand, "I see you're a graduate of West Point. Now, me, I had to work my way through college."

"Yeah!" Ralph grinned good-naturedly. "I saw you doing it two or three times and, as a matter of fact, through two or three schools."

"That ain't no lie." The Ball returned the grin. "And two or three times I could have taken ROTC and maybe gotten a Reserve commission. But the coaches were against it for more than one reason and, anyhow, it wasn't much of a prize. In most places it was called 'Bull' and got the razzberry."

The Ball swirled dwindling ice cubes in his glass and looked to see if we followed him. Ralph and I both indicated our understanding of the average prewar collegiate's revulsion against military training.

"Anyhow," resumed The Ball, "when I finished school—" He saw Ralph smile and corrected himself. "That is, up to the time I played my last college football game, I never wore khaki nor got any credits in Military Science and Tactics. Then, about a year ago, I was inducted. You probably read about it in the papers?"

We hadn't, but to save The Ball's feelings, we indicated that we had.

"Coming down to cases," The Ball reached down with both hands and lifted up his right knee, "most guys like me have a bum shoulder, a trick ankle or a bad knee, and this one of mine is about as bad as they come. It's been cut into by doctors plenty of times, and when I play ball I have to wear a steel brace or I couldn't stand on my feet."

There flashed into my mind a vivid picture of the last time I had seen The Ball going fifteen yards to pay dirt, carrying no less than three opponents along with him. Nevertheless, I kept my big mouth shut and let him continue.

"The docs didn't pay much attention to my knee when I was inducted, so I didn't make any fuss about it. Just went ahead and did the best I could. For short periods, like setting-up exercises and drills, I was OK. But those twenty-five-mile hikes and speed marches gave me hell. I'd have to sit up nights with hot towels around my leg to keep on going. But I did it and pretty soon I was a sergeant." The Ball smiled reminiscently. "It was sort of like making All-American. And soon after that they sent me to Officer Candidate School."

All good humor departed from The Ball's face. He regarded us with a bitterness hard to understand while going on to explain what had happened.

"That candidate school was like the 'Bull' in college, only more so. I counted cadence, sang marching songs and managed to stay in there pitching until my final physical exam. Then they found out about my bum knee and bounced me right out on my ear."

The Ball kneaded the knuckles of one hand into the palm of the other. He undoubtedly felt like punching somebody in the nose.

"Seems like I was good enough to carry a gun, sleep in a

foxhole and eat out of a mess kit, but my knee disqualified me from sitting at a desk, maybe, or riding in a limousine and having my meals brought to me at a table in the officers' club. So then I said 'to hell with it.' After the next long hike I didn't bother with hot towels around my knee. I just went to bed and next morning limped over to the hospital so they could take a look. Well, they not only looked, they took X-rays and when they developed the X-rays they went into a huddle. After that they came up with the verdict that it had all been a mistake. I not only wasn't good enough to be an officer, but I didn't even qualify as a soldier. So I thinks, 'Who am I to tell these guys their business?' and here I am."

He thumped his empty glass down on a near-by table.

"A lot of people are going to say I ran out on my country," he said bitterly. "That I pulled a fast one to get out of the Army, or else I couldn't be playing football. Well, you can tell 'em for me that I *can* play sixty minutes in the big-time with a week's rest in between, where I can't go all day long, every day in the week."

I could see that Ralph was sympathetically impressed, so I waited until we had thanked The Ball for our drinks and were outside before picking flaws in his statements.

"He didn't mention that he probably gets more pay for his sixty minutes on the gridiron than for a year in the Army."

"A guy has to eat," Ralph defended.

"Sure, but he could eat in the Army, doing limited service."

"Well, anyhow, there's nothing neurotic about The Ball."

"I'm not so sure about that!"

"You're not sure?" Ralph's eyes revealed the suspicion that I was getting a little off the beam myself. "What are you driving at?"

"Look," I said, "what's the difference between him and the rest of these fellows we've been looking at? He gets along all right until he doesn't want to any more, and then he quits."

"But he has a real injury," Ralph persisted.

"So do those other people, if you believe the psychiatrists," I pointed out. "It's all a matter of incentive. If they want to, badly enough, they can do anything, but when they don't, they go to a hospital."

Ralph muttered to himself for a moment or two and then shook his head. "You out-argue me on that one, but you don't convince me. Let's see some of the other front-page names we're supposed to look into."

We scanned the list until Ralph jabbed down a finger.

"Look! A jockey!"

"Sure enough."

"Why, it's Johnny! I remember when he won the Kentucky Derby." Ralph loved anything to do with horses. "How about seeing him next? Bet a nickel you don't find anything neurotic about him."

"OK," I agreed, "make it a nickel a throw on all of 'em. I'm already one up on The Cannon Ball."

"What a reckless gambler you are!" Ralph jeered. But he accepted the wager, and as it turned out he won his bet on Johnny. Try as I would, I couldn't find any sign of a neurosis in the quiet little man who had ridden a winner in one of turf-dom's greatest classics.

"There's nothing the matter with me," Johnny replied in response to our queries, "except I'm undersize and underweight. Of course, I have to be that way in my business, but some people act like they thought I'd been training all these years just to keep out of the draft."

"How tall are you, Johnny?" I asked.

"I'm four eleven and weigh one hundred and twelve. The Army says they don't have clothes small enough to fit me and that I'm not big enough to carry a rifle and a pack."

I tried to imagine Johnny with a sixty-pound pack and rifle on his back in the division of Jimmy-the-Hard, where it was a case of "no twenty-five-mile hike, no soldier." Obviously, Johnny didn't fit into any such picture as that, but just the same it seemed awfully foolish not to have taken Johnny in preference to some of the men we had seen in the service. Furthermore, Johnny was of the same opinion.

"I'm not saying I could make those hikes and do all the things the rest of the boys have to do. But I bet I could ride in the turret of a tank and shoot as good as the best of them."

"I bet you could too, Johnny," I agreed, "and I suppose there are a lot of other fellows around the tracks who have been turned down for the same reasons you were."

"Yes, but it wasn't as tough on them as on me."

"How is that?"

"Well, when a stable swipe or exercise boy gets turned down, nobody knows and nobody cares. But me, I was a Derby winner. I'm in the chips! So, when the Army turns me down, it comes out in the newspapers. That starts everybody talking and pretty soon they're trying to make it look like I did something crooked or bought myself out of it, or something. It gives me a pain."

I shot a quick look at Ralph and his eyes dared me to construe that last remark as an indication of psychoneurosis. I winked a reply and turned back to Johnny.

"Never mind," I consoled. "Before it's over they may be glad to have you.

"I hope so," he replied as we shook hands in parting, "I know they could use me somewhere."

It later turned out that we were both right, because it was not long before the Army Air Forces began looking frantically for men small enough to fit into the ball-turrets of their super-fortresses. But at that time, none of us knew it, so our departure was saddened by the wistful look on Johnny's face.

"You ought to pay me a dime on him," said Ralph.

"Tell you what I'll do," I said, pulling out our list again, "I'll play you double or nothing on the next one."

"You're on," Ralph accepted quickly. "Who is it?"

I pointed.

"Why you dirty robber!" he almost yelled.

"What's wrong?" I asked, as innocently as possible. "You know he was one of the greatest pitchers in the big leagues."

"Of course, I know it, just like you know they call him the Screw Ball!"

"That's probably because of the curves he throws."

"Oh sure!" Ralph snorted. "And I suppose that's why he was always being fined or suspended for doing crazy things. But anyhow—" A sudden thought struck Ralph and he brightened up. "I'll probably lose this one, but it will be worth it if he pulls one of his practical jokes on you."

But Screw Ball, much to Ralph's disappointment, showed no signs of levity during our somewhat brief interview. He was too apprehensive regarding its possible outcome.

"I got chronic otitis media," he said impressively, upon our asking the reason for his rejection.

He might have stumped us right there had we not ascertained the reason beforehand and looked it up in a medical dictionary.

"That means an opening or exposure of the middle ear, doesn't it?" I asked casually.

"Yeah, sure," replied Screw Ball, somewhat taken aback, "that's what it is."

"Does it hurt very much?" I asked, again casually.

"Well, no. That is, not all the time. " He regarded me somewhat apprehensively. "But the doctors say it makes me below the minimum standards for induction," he added hastily.

"Oh," I waved that aside airily, "they're always changing those, aren't they, Colonel?"

"Sure," Ralph played up, "whenever they need more men." Screw Ball looked from one to the other of us, a worried frown wrinkling his forehead.

"Of course," he said, "that ain't all that's wrong with me. My arm is awful stiff and I get bad headaches ever since I was beaned with a fast ball."

"That's tough," I sympathized. "But tell me, do the pains in your head ever get low down in your back and spread across into the groin?"

Screw Ball fidgeted uneasily. He looked at me suspiciously and then appealingly at Ralph. Evidently he feared a trap but didn't know which answer would be correct. Finally he made his decision.

"Yeah," he said, "sometimes they do."

Ralph lifted both hands, palms out, meaning "Kamerad!"

"That was a dirty trick to play on Screw Ball," he accused, once we were on our way again, "and just to win a bet."

"To prove that it had nothing to do with our bet, we'll double again on the next one. How about it?"

"It's a deal, only this time I do the picking."

"Fair enough," I said, handing him the list.

Ralph's choice was a man whom thousands of people had paid money to see and cheered when they saw him. He was tough and courageous, and he had been a fighter most of his life. Though well into the thirties, he was still known as "The Kid."

We found him on the second floor of a dilapidated old building, housing a dimly lighted, poorly ventilated gymnasium. It smelled of sweat, liniment and stale tobacco smoke. The Kid was shuffling about in ring togs and sweat shirt, shooting short hard punches at a heavy bag, almost as large as himself.

When we spoke to him The Kid ceased punishing the bag and half turned his head. But the flesh along his brows was so scarred and puffed out that his eyes were almost completely hidden. I couldn't tell whether he was looking at us or not.

"Are you lookin' to fix up a match?" he finally asked.

Neither Ralph nor I could think up just what to say, so The Kid turned all the way 'round and shuffled in our direction. When almost upon us he stopped, apparently noticing our uniforms for the first time.

"Oh," he said, holding out a hand encased in fingerless leather gloves, "you're Army guys." His heavy lips spread in a sparsely toothed smile. "They weighed me in for some kind of a go in the Army, but I guess I didn't make the weight. Say," a happy look spread over his battered features, "have youse come here to fix it up? Huh?"

"Well, Kid," I was able to say honestly enough, "we did come here to see what kind of shape you were in."

"In shape? Me?" The Kid had a rasping laugh. "Look!"

He ducked and weaved in a shuffling form of shadow boxing. He lashed out with both hands, then pursued and drove an imaginary opponent across the floor, ending up head-on against

the wooden wall of a small partition near the door of the
gymnasium.

"Have a heart, Cookie!" Ralph implored, tugging at my
sleeve. The poor Kid is walking on his heels. He's punch
drunk!"

"Jeepers!" I said in return. "Don't you suppose I can see
that? Show me how to get away without hurting The Kid's
feelings and I'll pay you double on our double bet."

But just then another man entered the gymnasium. His face
showed big and soft between a down-tilted hat and a vest on
which many a cigar had dripped its ashes. His little eyes caught
sight of us immediately and he walked forward without a glance
at The Kid who had backed away from the wall, still throwing
punches at thin air.

"Did you want to see me about The Kid?" Fat Face asked.
"I'm his manager."

At the sound of voices The Kid stopped swinging and shuffled
hastily over to join us.

"Maybe they'll give us a match, Mart," he said. "Don't worry
about the weight. I'll give away anything up to ten
pounds."

"OK, Kid," Fat Face waved him off, "better take a shower."

We stood silently as The Kid's feet shuffled to the door. There
he paused. "Make it up to fifteen pounds, Mart," he called, and
then was gone.

We stood in uncomfortable silence for a minute, while Fat
Face's eyes avoided ours.

"How long ago did the Army turn him down?" I finally
asked.

"Oh, two or three months."

"And how long ago did he go blind?" asked Ralph sharply.

"He ain't blind," Fat Face replied defensively, "he can see good enough under the ring lights."

"And how many more punches can he take before he's standing on a corner with a tin cup in his hand?" persisted Ralph.

Fat Face didn't like the look on Ralph's face, and neither did I.

"How about yourself?" I interposed. "Have you been called up?"

Fat Face looked uncomfortable. "I was rejected, too. I've got a bad heart."

Ralph muttered something under his breath to the effect that the only thing bad about Fat Face's heart was the size of it, whereupon I got him away from there as quickly as possible.

"Calm down," I entreated, "we're supposed to be conducting an inquiry, not starting private wars of our own."

"I know it, Cookie, but that burns me up. The Kid is all shot but his big slug of a manager not only lets him keep on taking a beating in the ring, he doesn't even want people to know what's wrong with The Kid for fear he won't get any more fights."

"Well, cool off," I said, reaching into my pocket, "and I'll pay off on our bet."

Ralph shook his head. "No," he said, "I don't want to take any money on The Kid. It wouldn't be lucky."

"Then how are we going to settle it?"

Ralph thought for a moment and then his face brightened. "Tell you what. We'll double it once more, then we'll put the rest of the names into a hat and the one we pull out is the one that decides the bet."

"It's a go!" I said.

So that was why our next interview took place in a New

York penthouse and had to do with the Muses. Our subject, or victim, was a man known far and wide to all hepcats and the disciples of jive.

He was slender and dark-haired and, at the time, badly in need of a shave. Instead of the immaculate starched shirt bosom and black tails in which he usually appeared in public, he wore a shabby dressing gown, grey slacks and sloppy slippers. He was nervous and seemed to have difficulty sitting still, or even in one place.

He offered us cigarettes from a handsome silver humidor and then took one for himself from a packet he carried in his pocket. After lighting up he seemed more calm and better able to talk.

"We are looking into the reasons for certain people being rejected for military service," I finally got around to telling our host.

A faint flush spread over his somewhat pallid features and he puffed deeper on his cigarette.

Happening to glance at Ralph I saw he had taken his own cigarette from his mouth and was gazing at it intently. Then I became conscious of a peculiar odor permeating the room and sniffed at my own cigarette. Our host was now relaxed, a small quirk of a smile lifting the corners of his mouth. Also the pupils of his eyes were contracting to almost nothing.

"Yes," he nodded unabashed, "I'm smoking marijuana. The doctors say I'm an addict. That's why the Army wouldn't take me."

Ralph and I were somewhat at a loss.

"How long have you been smoking the hemp?" I asked, for lack of something better to say.

"For several years," he replied, "I guess I need it to keep me going."

I didn't think he'd keep going very long at that rate but, after all, only one phase of it was any of my business.

"Didn't you want to go into the Army?"

He shrugged and said, "Not unless they let me have this stuff when I need it."

"They couldn't do that," I pointed out. "It's contrary to the Articles of War."

Again he shrugged. "In that case, I'd land up in a strait jacket inside of a week. Either that, or I'd desert until I got hold of some."

Ralph and I looked dubiously at each other. Certainly the Army didn't want to induct a man just to put him in a locked ward as a cure for marijuana. Nor for that matter did it want to take him to put him directly in the guardhouse as puishment for being an addict in civil life. We thought the matter over while going down in an elevator.

"The Army's a whole lot better off without him," I finally decided.

"Sure. No use in our washing dirty linen for the civil authorities," Ralph agreed. "But what I want to know is, do you call him a psychoneurotic?"

"Oh," I said, remembering our bet, "darned if I know. What do you say?"

Ralph cuffed back his cap. "I don't know either, but he's certainly some kind of a something. He probably could lay off the smoke if he wanted to badly enough."

"I suppose so," I conceded, "but he must be hitting the hemp as a mental escape from something. Evidently joining the Army wouldn't help him do that, so he doesn't want to give up the smoke."

"Huh! You sound like a psychiatrist. But doesn't that make

him the same as all those other guys who get sick or have something happen to them when they can't do what they want
to do?"

"Say, which side of this thing are you on now?" I demanded.

"Well, in my books this last guy is twice as bad as The Cannon Ball or Screw Ball. If they're psychos, this one is super-
psycho!"

"But we didn't decide definitely on them either," I pointed
out. "Let's call this one a draw, and redouble on the next one."

Ralph looked at me a little strangely. "OK. But we'd better
be settling our bet pretty soon."

That, unfortunately, was easier said than done. The next
drawing on rejects led us to the manager of a big league base-
ball team. He had a perforated eardrum. One of his star players suffered from a severe case of hammer-toes. Our quest took
us on—through the world of sports, the arts and sciences and
the hall of fame. We encountered epilepsy, syphilis, diabetes,
convulsions, hernias and hypertensions. All of them were technical disqualifications for military service, although not for some
of the violent occupations in which many of the sufferers
engaged.

"What gets me," said Ralph wearily, after a long and ardu-
ous series of interviews, "is how are we going to explain this
thing to the Chief? Actually, all these guys are below the minimum physical standards for service, but on the other hand there
isn't a one of them that couldn't perform some kind of military
duty."

"That's true," I admitted. "So all we can do is report the
truth."

"Well, I hope so!" Ralph was somewhat alarmed. "But just
what is the truth?"

"As I see it, all prominent citizens are more or less in the public spotlight. If one of them gets discharged or rejected, it comes out in the newspapers and people are only too willing to believe and even to say that some kind of underhand influence was employed. But while a handful of big shots are being let out or exempted, the same thing is happening to thousands of more obscure persons who wouldn't be news short of jumping off the Brooklyn Bridge. So, nobody pays any attention to them or cares whether they get into the Army or not."

"Go on," Ralph smiled, "tell me some more."

"It boils down to this. We can make soldiers out of any class of Americans, from bindle stiffs to millionaires, but in all classes there's bound to be a proportionate number unable or unwilling to serve their country. Multiply all the persons in each class by that ratio and you'll come pretty close to knowing how many soldiers and how many rejects you're going to end up with. And what's more, you've got to treat all rejects the same—just like you do the soldiers."

Ralph lit a cigarette. "What you're getting at is, if no fuss is made over exempting a thousand poor guys with high blood pressure, we shouldn't punish one other guy with hypertension by inducting him into the Army just because he is rich or is in the news. Is that it?"

"That," I admitted, "is it!"

Ralph took a couple of drags and then nodded his head. "Sounds like sense. You better make a report while the idea is hot."

I reached for a phone, dialed a number, got still a second number and identified myself. For the time it took someone at the other end to switch on a recorder I waited, then was told to go ahead. I talked for five minutes. Briefly, I received an acknowledgment, along with further instructions. The line went dead before I could hang up.

I turned to Ralph, who had moved over to gaze from a window down onto the blacked-out main stem of our leading metropolis.

"Ralphie," I said, "do you know what a Processing Center is?"

"No. What is it?'"

"It's a place where they keep the boys who come down with salt-water fever when they see a transport. We have to go to one tomorrow."

"As inmates or to inspect?" Ralph grinned.

"The boss didn't say, but I suppose it still has to do with psychoneurotics."

"What do you mean, 'still'?" Ralph jeered. "Are you trying to gyp me into paying that doubling-up bet on whether or not our athletic and other friends were psychoneurotics because they had some ailment to keep them out of the Army?"

"You'll have to admit there weren't many of them who couldn't have gotten in if they'd wanted to badly enough. But I'm not asking you to pay anything. I'll toss you for whatever the bet amounts to."

Ralph looked at me intently for a moment. "Do you know how much it is?"

"Oh, a couple of dollars, I suppose. We only started with a nickel."

"Oh yeah?" Ralph showed me some figures on a slip of paper. "Start with five and double each time for fifteen times, then see what you get."

"Suffocating smoke screens!" I cried in amazement. "Eight hundred and nineteen dollars and twenty cents. I didn't know we were talking about any such money as that."

"I didn't think you did," replied Ralph. "It's like those ratios of classes you were sounding off about just now. For every person we saw with disqualifying ailments, there are probably some eight hundred of the same kind we didn't see."

"Well," I hedged, "I don't have the eight hundred dollars, but I do have nineteen dollars and twenty cents. I'll buy a drink if you're willing to call it even."

"Double or nothing," said Ralph firmly, "I'll buy one too."

I reached for my hat. "What are we waiting for?"

CHAPTER 6

GANGPLANK FEVER

~~~~~~

SOLDIERS WHO RAN AWAY FROM THEIR OUTFITS A FEW days before boarding a transport for overseas were not looked upon with favor by the War Department. All of them caught west of the Mississippi were sent to a camp in California, and all caught east of the river were sent to the East Coast Processing Center at Camp Edwards on Cape Cod. Camp Edwards looked neat and orderly on a flat, sandy plateau, but the terrain drained off to the northeast, and right where the drainage turned to mud was the Processing Center.

Ralph Bing and I sank ankle deep as we stepped from our car and stood gazing at the gloomy rows of unpainted cantonment completely inclosed by two lines of high, barbed-wire fencing. At hundred-yard intervals along the outer fence were tall wooden towers in each of which sat a soldier behind a machine gun.

"Cripes!" Ralph ejaculated. "Do you suppose they keep Americans in a place like that?"

"I don't know just what you'd call those lads but there certainly are plenty of them," I said, indicating several large groups of denim-clad men moving about under the watchful eyes of a dozen sentries.

Just then a hard-bitten major appeared before us to render a punctilious salute. "Would you care to see the commanding officer, sir?" he asked.

The commanding officer, we replied, was just the person we wanted to see, so the major led us to a wooden structure standing like an oasis in the surrounding mud.

89

A colonel, two lieutenant colonels and a captain were waiting inside to receive us. There was a reserved air of cultivated hardness and formality about them as we exchanged introductions.

"How many men are in confinement here?" I started the conversation.

"About 2,800," replied the colonel.

"How long do you keep them?"

"As long as it takes to find out who they are and what outfit they belong to. Then we take them under guard and put them on a ship." The colonel's words were short and emotionless.

"Won't they tell you who they are?" asked Ralph.

"They tell us all kinds of things," the colonel's lips almost softened into a smile, "but you can't believe any of it. They think it's smarter to tell a lie, even when the truth would be more to their advantage."

I wondered just what kind of men we were dealing with. "Do you have a psychiatrist on duty here?"

"Yes, sir," spoke up the captain who was present. "I am a psychiatrist." He, too, was a hardboiled sort of individual and the Army uniform he wore somehow did not seem to suit him.

"Did you practice psychiatry before you came into the Army?" I inquired.

"Yes, sir. For eight years I was the psychiatrist at a state penitentiary," and he named the state.

A light began to dawn upon me.

I looked at the colonel. "Have you had previous experience in a penal institution?"

"We all have," he stated flatly. "I was a warden for twelve years."

I looked at the two lieutenant colonels, who nodded in agreement. "Then this place is operated along the same lines as a penitentiary?"

"Well," spoke up one of the lieutenant colonels, evidently the executive officer, "we handle the same kind of people. In fact, some of them are the same!"

I stared inquiringly at the colonel.

"Do you actually recognize some of the men coming through here as those you have had previously in a penitentiary?"

"Yes, we recognize some of them, even though they frequently appear under different names." From his desk the colonel lifted a file of papers. "Here is the case of a man named Redeni. He served nine years in a penitentiary and was out only three weeks before he was inducted into the Army. Since then he has been AWOL four times for periods of from one to three months, the last time being just before his outfit went overseas."

"Looks like he was boning for a dishonorable discharge," said Ralph.

This time the colonel's lips actually twisted sardonically into a one-sided smile. "Nothing would please him more. Practically all our inmates will do anything in their power to keep from being sent overseas. They break windows, tear down walls, use abusive language to officers and sentries, disobey orders and everything else in the hope of being sent to jail here instead of being put aboard a transport."

"Don't you court-martial them for such things?" I inquired.

"Indeed we do! And when they get too tough we even put them in solitary confinement. But the main thing is to get them on the first available transport going overseas. That is what they are determined to avoid and that is what the War Department is equally determined shall be done with them."

"Pretty hard on the theater commanders who have to take men like that," commented Ralph.

"But they were their men to begin with," the executive officer pointed out.

"You say these men would do anything to keep from being shipped overseas?" I changed to another line of thought, "What can they do when they're in a barbed-wire inclosure?"

The colonel's bleak face resumed its grimness. "First, all that had them broke their glasses or threw away their false teeth at the last moment, knowing it was against regulations to send men overseas who needed such things and didn't have them."

"Why, the sons-of-guns," cried Ralph. "Who would have thought of that?"

"The War Department hadn't," continued the colonel, "until we called the matter to their attention. Then the regulations were changed so that any man who had once been fitted with glasses or false teeth could be sent overseas whether or not he still had them when his time came to go."

"But there are comparatively few with glasses and false teeth. What did the rest of them do?" I asked.

The colonel looked significantly at the captain who, catching the signal, smiled wanly.

"They pulled a fast one on me," he admitted. "There's hardly a group comes in that one of them doesn't have a case of gonorrhea. Well, the others would induce him into a synthetic ejaculation and then use the semen to infect themselves."

Ralph and I stared at each other in amazement. We wondered if we were hearing about people supposed to be soldiers.

"Of course," the doctor hastened to explain, "we soon cured that by giving them a physical the first thing upon arrival. We also got the War Department to change the regulations on that, too, so men can be sent overseas now, even if they do have a venereal disease."

"They also have some other tricks," said the colonel, taking over the tale, "but mostly they hide. We've dug them out of bins under the coal and rooted them out of caves and tunnels dug underneath their barracks. We even had to pull down the inner walls inside some of the barracks because men had wedged themselves in so tightly they couldn't get out again and might have suffocated."

"But how do they know when to hide? Surely they don't know when a transport is going to leave, do they?"

The colonel shook his head ruefully. "No, but they can make a pretty good guess. You see, a few hours before we put them on a train we have to issue them uniforms and equipment. That's the giveaway and they immediately take advantage of it—if they can."

"How can you stop them?" asked Ralph eagerly.

Again the sardonic quirk twisted the colonel's lips. "Inside the main inclosure, you'll find a smaller compound we have recently built. It's right alongside one of the main gates so the men never know whether a group is being marched outside for some detail or into the compound. They pass it every day, but once in that compound they can't get away to hide before we take them out and put them on a train."

"Do any of them try to bolt once they're on the outside?" I queried.

"Only when they're being taken to the port. Then they'll jump out of windows, off of moving trucks and even over the sides of harbor boats."

"They must be crazy," said Ralph in disgust.

I turned to the captain. "How about it? Are any of them psychotics?"

He blinked his surprise. "Well, there may be some border-line cases, but I would say that most of them are constitutional psychopaths, or have a psychopathic personality."

"Huh!" said Ralph, not wishing to admit our unfamiliarity with these new terms. "We find psychotics in locked wards and neurotics in the open wards of hospitals. Why is it the constitutional psychopaths, as you call them, are in jail?"

The captain peered at our insignia of branch. Evidently he was wondering if, in addition to being inspectors general, either of us was a member of the Medical Department.

"Of course," he began, a little cautiously, "the constitutional psychopath is not psychotic because he is not insane. Neither is he a psychoneurotic because he is not suffering from any functional nervous disorder. Actually, the psychopath is the rebellious type of person who defies authority. He is not normal because of his anti-social behavior."

"Just what do you call anti-social?" I asked.

"Oh, homosexuality, prostitution, pathological lying and criminal violations of established laws and orders."

"Then, as I see it, there are three general groups in the psychiatric field," said Ralph, getting ready to check them off on his fingers. "First, the psychotic, who is insane and not responsible for what he does; second, the psychoneurotic, who, under certain kinds of stress, develops a nervous disorder which prevents him from carrying on; and third, the psychopath who doesn't want to do something and just says, 'to hell with it'!"

The captain regarded Ralph with considerable interest. "I don't believe that answer would satisfy a board of medical examiners but it sounds all right to me."

"Well, now that we have that settled," I said, "let's take a look at some of these 'go to hell' guys."

They turned out to be little different in aspect from the persons we had seen in the NP wards, except the latter had been more obsequious and complaining, whereas inmates of the Processing Center were prone to be boastful and defiant.

Our first interview was with the current idol of the Center. He had been AWOL for three months, impersonating an officer and cashing rubber checks from coast to coast.

"They wouldn't send me to Officer Candidate School," he gave as his reason, "and I wouldn't do KP duty and dirty fatigue work, so I went out to have a good time."

The next man was a large, burly Negro, who had escaped on seven different occasions while being taken from the Center to a port of embarkation.

"Dey ain't gonna get me overseas," he shook his head obstinately. "Dey may think dey is, but dey ain't! Ah kin fool dem as long as dey fools wid me!"

Family trouble was the excuse offered by a small, pimply-faced individual with unkempt hair and dirty fingernails.

"I was home on emergency furlough and used up all my money on doctor bills. My wife had given away our oldest child and was trying to find a home for the other two so she could go to a boy friend in California. I had to stay home to straighten things out."

Another variation on a more amusing scale was offered when one man stated quite seriously, "I went AWOL because my intended wife was sick and also pregnant."

That was followed by a group who made such statements as: "I can't fire a gun or go under fire." "I can't kill anyone, I don't believe in killing people." "I was afraid, I guess, so I went home." And lastly, "I wanted to see my girl; I don't like the Army and I'm scared of water."

Then came a diversion. Five men appeared of their own accord to make a complaint!

"What's your trouble?" I asked, preparing myself for anything.

"We never did no AWOL an' they shouldn't put us here!" declared their spokesman, a short, broad-faced blonde with a stubble beard. The other four stood behind their leader, stolid in the manner of the foreign-born when in the presence of authority. Yet they seemed placidly sure that their wrongs were now to be adjusted.

"How did you get here?" I queried.

"The captain he say always we dumb. But we no go AWOL, we no get drunk, we no do nothing. Then we come to place for catch boat. The captain he send for us. He say boat no go 'til morning. He give us each two dolla. He say, 'Go New York, have good time, come back in morning'." The man paused and shook his head reproachfully.

"Well," I urged, "what happened?"

"We come back in morning; the boat she gone, the captain he gone, everything gone! They put us in guardhouse!"

A stifled exclamation came from Ralph but when I turned sharply he was having a fit of coughing. I assured the five men that we would look into their case as soon as possible, and they departed, quite satisfied.

Then came a series of interviews with men whose stories had a familiar ring. According to each one he had gone AWOL because he had a bad back, a headache, bad feet or other physical ailment and the Army doctors wouldn't do anything about it. They certainly sounded as much like psychoneurotics as any we had heard. I saw that Ralph, like myself was getting more and more puzzled, so I stopped the interviews.

"I thought you said these men were not psychoneurotic," I said accusingly to the doctor.

He straightened up defensively, "What I said was that they were constitutional psychopaths."

"But they have psychoneurotic symptoms," Ralph pointed out.

The captain shook his head. "It may have sounded that way to you, but in the case of those men, there were no functional disorders present. Also, you will notice that the story they gave with regard to a physical ailment was offered as an excuse for having committed an offense."

Ralph propped his chin in his hands. "It seems to me that a psychoneurotic is a person who gets sick and can't do what he is supposed to do, while the psychopath gets sick after he's done something he isn't supposed to do. Where's the real difference?"

The captain sorted over some words very carefully before answering. "The difference is that the psychopaths you have seen are not afflicted with functional disorders. They are not sick in a physical way, but are characterized by behavior disorders."

"But a lot of them say they are sick," Ralph persisted.

The captain shrugged. "They are not, however, unless they make themselves so."

"What do you mean by that?" I challenged.

"Well, if a man's pulse and blood pressure, for instance, went extremely high under stress and remained that way long after being removed from the cause of his trouble, that man would be sick for reasons beyond his control. Another man, however, who took something to cause his blood pressure to rise and his pulse to be accelerated as a means to avoid hazardous duty, would be doing so deliberately. The one would be an indication of psychoneurosis whereas the other would more aptly be a manifestation of psychopathic proclivities."

Ralph rubbed the tip of his nose with the forefinger of one hand. "Huh!" he grunted reflectively. "The guy who shoots himself in the foot to keep from going overseas is court-martialed, even though he is crippled from his wound. But the lad who gets the pip at sight of a transport is taken to a hospital and ends up with a discharge—to say nothing of a pension. Is that fair?"

I avoided that question by asking another of the captain. "Have you had any cases of men taking drugs or anything else to induce illness?"

He nodded grimly. "There have been several. Their records were sent to the New York Port of Embarkation."

I cast an inquiring look at Ralph.

"Let's go," he nodded cheerfully, "I haven't been near a transport for over a month. Maybe I'll break out in a rash when I see one."

The colonel and his entire staff accompanied us to our car. "Is there anything else we can get for you?" he asked.

"How about those five men who claimed their captain sent them to New York so the boat would leave without them?" I asked. "Do you know anything about it?"

The colonel looked at his executive officer, who shifted his feet uncomfortably.

"From what we can find out, I really think they are telling the truth," he admitted.

Ralph threw back his head for a hearty laugh and said, "I think that captain was pretty smart. He ought to get a medal."

"He's lucky not to get a court-martial," I contradicted. "Just what do you propose to do about those men, colonel?"

"Why—," the colonel was a little flustered, "I could put them on a ship tomorrow."

"That will solve their problem," I approved, "and we will take care of the captain."

Seeing a sardonic question forming in Ralph's merry eyes, I looked about hastily for a means of changing the subject. Just then a detail of soldiers came around one corner of the stockade and halted to change guards in one of the towers.

"Tell me something else," I said. "How many men are required to guard and administer these prisoners of yours?"

"About eighteen hundred," said the colonel, patly.

"Eighteen hundred?" Ralph repeated, in surprise. "Why, that's more than one guard for every two prisoners."

"Yes, but you must remember we have three shifts of guards for each twenty-four hours, besides needing extra guards for every work detail that leaves the inclosure. We also have to have instructors to carry out the training program required of us."

"Training?" I was startled. "What kind of training?"

"All kinds," the second lieutenant colonel who, up until then had not entered the conversation, now stepped forward. "We have physical training, close-order drill, parades and even rifle marksmanship."

"But why?" I persisted. "They were all trained and ready for overseas before they came here."

"We have to do it so they won't forget," the lieutenant colonel replied earnestly.

"Are the men who give the instruction qualified for overseas duty themselves?" asked Ralph.

"They have to be," interposed the colonel. "If they weren't, they couldn't handle these prisoners. Also, we have to do something to keep these men busy or they would get completely out of hand."

Ralph shook his head sadly. "Just the same, it's a hell of waste of good soldiers," he said, getting into our automobile.

"One more thing," I paused on the running board to address the colonel. "Do you keep any track of the prisoners' nationalities?"

"No sir, we don't," the colonel was puzzled. "But I think nearly all of them were born right here in America."

"Thanks," I said, getting in beside Ralph and closing the door. "We were wondering about that when we drove up."

Ralph muttered to himself as the car lurched through muddy ruts to the nearest pavement.

"They may have been born here," he finally blurted out, "but you can't convince me they are Americans."

"Perhaps when they finally go overseas they do better," I suggested.

Ralph looked up with sudden interest. "Say, do you suppose we could go over and find out?"

For a moment I was too surprised to answer. Then the idea took hold of my imagination.

"Why not? Our directive doesn't say we can't."

"No," Ralph admitted, "but it doesn't say we can, either. I don't want to be picked up and thrown into one of those barbed-wire corrals."

"Maybe we'll find out something at the Port that will give us a good reason to go over," I said hopefully. And as a matter of fact, we did.

The New York Port of Embarkation was commanded by a

two-star general known to the cavalry and a good many other people as "Hy." He was easygoing on the surface and had a habit of commiserating with himself over all the difficulties besetting him. He always sounded so hard pressed that it wasn't until long afterwards his listeners suddenly woke up to the fact that they had done things just to help the poor guy that maybe they never would have done without being softened up with sympathy.

Ralph and I had listened to many a tale of Hy's woes, so we tried to unload our own troubles first. But you can't beat a professional. Hy nearly wept at mention of the Processing Center and its inmates. He sent hastily for his director of personnel, his surgeon and his secretary.

"You fellows have always kept me out of jail before," he poured the honey to me and Ralph, "so I'm counting on you to help me now."

We assured him we were ready to assist in any way we could. "What's the trouble?" I asked.

He took some papers from his secretary, who evidently had been briefed on just what was coming up.

"I've just had a couple of civilian doctors arrested," said Hy plaintively.

"Sure enough?" I exclaimed with interest. "What for?"

"Well, one of 'em was selling courses in psychoneurosis. For anywhere from two hundred to a thousand dollars he'd guarantee to coach anyone so they would either be rejected or discharged from the Army as a psychoneurotic."

"I'll be darned!" I said in amazement. "What about the other one?"

Hy picked up one of the papers his secretary had brought in. "Look at this," he said, "it's a letter one of our censors caught."

Ralph and I moved close so we could read it together.

Darling Bila:

It was marvelous to speak with you over the phone. You did not understand what I tried to tell you so I'll explain everything and please read very carefully. I went to Dr. Moluar and paid him to tell me how to help get you out of the Army.

Put salt in your black coffee. It must be black coffee. Put a little more than ½ teaspoon of salt in the black coffee. It will make you sick, vomit and dizzy and the front and back of your head hurt very much.

Inclosed is a small package. The name of it is saffron. You put a pinch of this in your mouth and swallow it with milk. Do this twice a day. It will make you turn yellow. The doctors in the Army will never find out what is wrong with you and what makes you yellow. Dr. Moluar says if you do all this you will be out of the Army in three months.

Be very careful that no one sees you doing this. Don't tell your best trusted buddies about it. Keep on the safe side. God will help you to come home if you do all this, but you got to be careful they don't catch you or they'll make your life miserable.

We all miss you very much so get busy.

All our love to you,
MOTHER AND THE FAMILY.

"Well," said Ralph, looking up hopefully. "What happened to Darling Bila and Dr. Moluar?"

"The FBI has Dr. Moluar and Darling Bila is on his way overseas," replied Hy. "Now, here's another one."

Ralph and I bent our heads over a second file. It consisted of a series of brief letters, but they told a full tale.

Dear Dan:

Do you know what you could do if you wanted to keep from going overseas? Start going on sick call complaining from terrible headaches. Tell them stories that you can't bend down because everything goes round; tell them you are getting nervous because you wake up a few times during the night without any reason. Tell them whatever you want until you get something. If you want to know more come here and meet Dr. Lockwood.

Your loving brother,

BEN.

Hello Dan:

How are you *soldier?* In two weeks I am going to be a civilian. I get discharged from the Army tomorrow. I'll leave for home within two weeks. But I must see you first and take you to Dr. Lockwood. He fixed me and he can fix you. If you don't have $200 I'll loan it to you. Please Dan plead with your CO for a pass. Beg the son of a bitch. I want you to see Dr. Lockwood. Boy, do I feel like a million. Whoopee! It's too good to be true. Please tell your CO it's very urgent. Nothing more to say but come soon. Good luck.

Your brother,

BEN.

Dear Mother:

I went to see Ben. I'm glad the kid pulled the swindle. There isn't a thing wrong with him. I was with him eight hours. He must have done some swell acting. I took some lessons myself. You'll hear from me soon.

Love,

DAN.

Dear Dan:

Something terrible has happened. I heard from Ben and he said he won't be discharged. That's an awful disappointment for all of us. Please do me a favor and find out if men on limited duty can be sent overseas. Dr. Lockwood says now he will get Ben marked limited duty. As soon as you find out for sure let me know at once and in detail form.

Love,

MOTHER.

Dear Dan:

My discharge went through a loophole but I am going to continue complaining to see if the bastards won't give me one yet. If they don't I'm going over the hill. They won't get me over there to be shot. Do you still have any patriotic ideas? I hope not! ! !

BEN.

Dear Mother:

I just heard terrible news. A guy wrote and said Ben was suddenly shipped out; he thought, overseas! It don't seem possible they would be so cruel as to send a man who acted so sick as Ben. I went to see the medical officer today to find out what the disposition of my own case is. As soon as the Xrays of my back are finished I'll know what's what. I hope they say I'm not eligible for overseas duty. There isn't anything wrong but I may have convinced the major; at least I hope so.

Love and kisses,

DAN.

"Well," Ralph spoke up first, "I don't see anything in this stuff to worry about. You've got the goods on these people."

"Oh, it's not only them that bother me." Hy opened the middle drawer of his desk, took out a plug of tobacco and daintily nibbled off a small corner. "It's all the other men like those you saw in the Processing Center that I've sent overseas who worry me."

I saw the old boy was leading up to something so I asked cautiously, "What about them?"

"When this thing first started," he began, "we didn't have any procedure set up to get rid of men who jumped ship or got saltwater fever. Pretty soon I had so many there weren't enough barracks to hold them all. They were driving everyone crazy. Then, about a month ago, I induced the War Department to let me use them to fill requisitions for overseas replacements.

"What's wrong with that?" asked Ralph.

Hy opened the right-hand drawer of his desk, pulled out a package of cigarettes and tore off the top.

"It's all right, I guess," he said, passing the cigarettes around. "Only I was so glad to be rid of those people I shipped all I could round up at one time."

Ralph and I digested that while lighting our cigarettes.

"How many were there?" I asked.

"Oh, just a few thousand."

Ralph whistled. "And all those birds went to one theater?"

"We only had requisitions for replacements from one

theater," spoke up Hy's director of personnel, who had not spoken until that moment.

Hy threw away his half-smoked cigarette, again reached into a drawer, drew out a cigar, bit off one end and returned the rest. The director of personnel subsided.

"What do you want us to do?" I asked Hy.

"I thought if you fellows were making a complete study of all this business you'd have to go overseas to finish it up. I knew you wouldn't mind explaining to General Ike and the rest of them over there about my having to get rid of all those people because I didn't have room for them any more."

Ralph opened his mouth to speak but I kicked him on the shin, hard.

"Sure! We'd be glad to, General," I hastened to say, "Only we couldn't go without authority from Washington."

Hy took out another cigarette and lit it. "When I heard you fellows were at the Processing Center I called Washington and asked if you couldn't be sent overseas to see what happens to those fellows when they get there."

Ralph's mouth dropped open a foot.

"What did they say?" I managed to ask weakly.

"Oh, they thought it was a good idea."

I got to my feet. "Come on, Ralph. We'd better go out and buy some water wings!"

"Don't forget to tell General Ike how it was about those replacements," pleaded Hy.

"I won't forget!" I assured him.

Once outside Hy's office, Ralph and I paused to gaze at each other dazedly.

"Well," Ralph's grin suddenly appeared, "we said we wanted to go overseas."

CHAPTER 7

PASS ALONG THE BUCK

~~~~~~

THE FOUR-MOTORED PLANE IN WHICH RALPH BING AND I had crossed the Atlantic banked slightly for a slow, wide turn and then leveled off again. Peeking over my shoulder through the small window behind me I could see nothing but mist and fog swirling by. We were in a world of moisture with no sky, no horizon and, worst of all, no good mother earth in sight. And we didn't have enough gasoline to go on forever!

All the passengers sat quietly in their aluminum bucket seats with that distant, preoccupied look of people communing with themselves—and possibly saying a silent prayer or two on the side. Over the forward door of the cabin a red-lighted sign warned us not to smoke and to keep our safety belts fastened.

"Cookie, where did you say we were going to land?"

"Prestwick," I tried to keep my voice at a normal pitch but my mouth and throat were so dry the word came none too clearly.

Ralph cast a swift glance through his own little window. "You wouldn't want to bet on it, would you?"

Before I could frame a suitable reply the nose of the plane tilted downward. We all looked out eagerly and hopefully. The solid well of mist was changing to streamers. Below was a smudge of brown, then green. A house flashed beneath us, some trees; the right wing of our plane barely scraped over a bouldered hill, we just missed a fence and then a concrete landing strip was sliding by right below us.

As the wheels touched, bounced and then clung snugly, the

passengers all exchanged tight little grins of assurance. It was all right and we hadn't been frightened at all. Not much!

Soon we were unloaded, herded into a dining room and fed powdered eggs, slightly scorched toast with marmalade and a liquid resembling coffee, at least in color. A little strange to our taste but pleasant to eat, just to be eating.

"Who is it we are supposed to see over here?" asked Ralph, having finished his share of the none too plentiful rations placed before us.

"Darned if I know," I said, lighting a cigarette to rid myself of the taste left by powdered eggs. "Whoever remained in command after General Eisenhower invaded North Africa, I suppose. We are trying to find out what happened to that bunch of constitutional psychopaths shipped out of New York from the East Coast Processing Center. Remember?"

"And we are also supposed to explain why they were sent over all in one shipment. Remember?" Ralph mocked. "What I'm wondering is, to whom do we have to explain it?"

"Look," I said, "perhaps we won't have to explain it to anybody; or at least, not until we know what became of them. They were equipped and clothed just like any other soldiers coming over, so maybe no one here knew the difference."

Ralph grinned. "You don't really believe that, do you?"

"No, but it doesn't cost anything to hope," I said, getting up from the table. "Let's see how we are going to get to London."

At operations we discovered that our passage had already been booked on the night train out of Glasgow.

There is one nice thing about British sleeping cars; you have a room to yourself with all accessories. I got a good night's rest after our transatlantic flight in a bucket seat. And it stood me in good stead for what we encountered the next day.

A young lieutenant with a car met our train and took us at once to an American officers' club on Park Lane, right across from Hyde Park. This four-story stone edifice had once been the palatial residence of a British tycoon who had made his money somewhere in Rhodesia.

The room assigned me was about the same size as my entire apartment back in Washington and, in addition, there was a bathroom with a pink marble tub. All in all, a quite comfortable place except that from the windows I looked directly across at three other houses completely gutted by bombs. A gentle reminder that a war was going on and that the lieutenant was waiting downstairs to take us to headquarters.

Grosvenor Square, where an American flag floated over a large corner building, was not far away. Sandbags protected the lower windows and a temporary vestibule of concrete had been erected around the entrance. But inside were carpets, electric lights, marble stairways and elevators. Also, there were some pretty nice looking British girls in uniforms answering telephones and tapping away at typewriters.

Ralph nudged me in the ribs. "I bet there aren't any psychoneurotics around here," he said, *sotto voce*.

"Don't be too sure," I replied, "we haven't had a chance to talk to anyone yet."

We didn't have long to wait. The general in command of the area was known as "J. C. Himself," and he met us outside the door of his office.

"Come right in," he invited affably, "and tell me what I can do for you."

His words and mouth smiled, but his eyes gave the impression of being on watch behind a wide moat with the drawbridge up. Nevertheless, he listened attentively while we told him of our search into the fields of psychiatry as well as our mission to ascertain what had become of the two or three thousand constitutional psychopaths shipped out of New York in the not too distant past.

"Sorry, old man," J. C. shook his head regretfully, "but that sounds like a medical problem to me. Perhaps you had better see our Surgeon."

"Yes, sir. We will talk to him about the psychoneurotics, but we thought you might tell us what was done with that big bunch of replacements from the Processing Center."

It seemed to me that in addition to the drawbridge, J. C. was slowly lowering a portcullis before his eyes.

"There are so many shipments coming in, I'm afraid I don't keep track of them all," he said deprecatorily.

"But you must remember this one," I persisted, "because it was rather a peculiar set-up."

"My personnel officer handles all matters of that kind," he said, a little less affably, and I began to see the ramparts of his mind across the moat.

"Then you don't remember anything about that particular group?" I made one last try.

"Young man," there was no longer any cordiality in his voice, "we all have a task of great magnitude to perform over here and I hold each staff officer responsible for his own department. If you are interested in personnel, consult with my G-1."

Ralph and I could take a hint when it was spoken as plainly as that, so we rose to our feet, saluted in farewell and got the hell out of there.

"Well," Ralph chuckled, "that's the first time I ever heard a fellow called 'old man' and 'young man' by the same guy in less than five minutes' time."

"Yeah," I said, "but it was probably because there's something screwy about this whole thing."

"How do you mean?"

"Remember at Prestwick how we said it would be nice if these people never found out they had gotten those two or three thousand ship jumpers old Hy sent over all at one time?"

"Sure."

"Did we think it was possible for them not to have found out about it?"

"I certainly didn't think so."

"Well, do you think so now?"

Ralph pulled at his chin with thumb and finger. "I see what you mean, all right. But maybe, like the big shot just told us, he leaves all such things to his G-1."

"There's one way of finding out," I said, walking across the corridor to where an office directory hung beside the elevator.

The office of the Assistant Chief of Staff, G-1, was two floors up and the man himself was an officer I hadn't seen in fifteen years.

"Well, for Pete's sake," he said with some astonishment, after we had introduced ourselves and I had recalled to his mind the last time we had served together, "what brings you fellows over here?"

"Well, Ossie," I said, giving him the nickname he had gone by in the past, "we're looking for a large shipment of replacements that came over here a couple of months past."

"Replacements?" Ossie rearranged some papers on his desk that seemed to have been doing all right in the first place. "What kind of replacements?"

I looked at Ossie a little more closely. It appeared almost as though there was some perspiration on his forehead, which was strange, since the room was far from warm.

"This was a mixture of all kinds, Ossie," I said, "Air, Ground and Service Forces men, all in one bunch. Somewhere around two or three thousand. Your people probably have a record of it in the files."

Ossie looked out the window, his lips pursed in thought. "Seems to me I do remember that there was such a shipment," he finally said.

"There isn't any doubt about the men being shipped," Ralph replied dryly. "The question is, what became of them?"

"We-e-ell," Ossie regarded us from the corners of his eyes, "you see, just about that time General Eisenhower cabled us to send him all the replacements we had available. The shipment you're speaking of had just reached port, so we immediately turned those ships around and sent them right on to North Africa."

"Holy smokes," Ralph breathed, "without even letting the men get off long enough to stretch their legs?"

"There wasn't time. General Eisenhower said he needed replacements just as soon as we could get them there."

We regarded each other for awhile and then I reached for my hat. "Ossie," I asked, "was there time enough for you to have seen their service records?"

"Oh, no," he replied virtuously. "But, of course, our people at the port had to execute a transfer for them."

That did it. I got up and walked to the door.

"Ossie," I looked back earnestly, "if I were you, I think I'd stay out of North Africa for awhile."

"I've thought of that," he admitted. "Right now the climate might be bad."

"Huh!" Ralph grunted, as we walked over to the elevator. "For him I bet the climate would be terrible."

"And for us, it won't be much better," I added.

Ralph raised his brows inquiringly. "Do we follow that gang right down to their final assignments?"

I pulled a piece of paper labeled "Secret" from my inner pocket. "In addition to a survey regarding psychoneurotics, you will ascertain the general disposition, utilization and subsequent evaluation of those men included in shipment two one one," I read.

"O.K.," Ralph shrugged. "Then we go to North Africa."

"But not," I said, "before we see the Surgeon."

"About psychoneurotics, I suppose. But I still don't see any reason for anyone having psychoneurosis over here," he cast an appraising eye at a couple of passing secretaries.

"Let's not get mixed up in any more military secrets than we have to," I said, grasping him firmly by the arm, "and particularly around the headquarters of old J. C. himself."

"Why, Cookie," Ralph protested, "you know I'm thinking only scientific thoughts!"

"Of course!" I agreed. "But just keep 'em scientific until after we've seen the medicos."

We found that the Surgeon held office in a building about two blocks away. Having shown our identification cards we were permitted to enter and climb two flights of stairs.

When we finally entered the unimposing office of the man we had come to see I received a shock. The Surgeon had been a classmate of mine at both the Command and General Staff School and the Army War College. But what really stunned me was the fact that he was drinking tea!

"My God, Paul," I exclaimed, "are you sick?"

He countered with a few words of profane welcome and then poured both Ralph and me a portion of the beverage. We accepted more out of curiosity than inclination.

"And now," he said, when we were all comfortable and cozy, "what kind of business are you fellows over here on, if any?"

It was too good an opportunity to pass up, so I nonchalantly crossed my legs and said, "Oh, we're just over here to find out what percentages of your casualties are psychiatric cases; what categories they are in with respect to anxiety state, traumatic, conversion hysteria, hypochondriases, neurasthenia, obsessional and depressive; and also, whether or not you are using the pentothal and electro-shock methods of treatment."

Paul choked over a mouthful of tea, coughed a couple of times and then regarded me with a baleful air while regaining his breath.

"Even if you know what you're talking about, Cookie, which I doubt very much," he managed to say, "what the hell business has your department got mixing into psychiatry?"

I shrugged. "Mostly because the Chief of Staff told us to. There is a group of top flight neuropsychiatrists conducting a big study in the Zone of Interior and I was elected a member of the group on the supposition that if I could understand what it was all about, then anybody could."

"Not a bad theory," Paul retorted dryly, and then turned suspiciously to Ralph, with whom it was his first meeting. "Are you a medical officer?"

Ralph grinned in negation. "Nope, I'm just a doughboy following Cookie around to keep him out of trouble and picking up what information I can on the side."

Paul shook his head gloomily. "My God, next they'll be sending quartermasters out to study surgery."

"Then you don't think we are going to learn very much?" I demanded.

"No," he declared quite frankly, "do you?"

"Oh," I said airily, "we pick up a little information here and there as we go along."

Paul regarded me intently for a moment and then burst into one of those contagious laughs which endeared him to his friends. "Then for Heaven's sake let me in on it because all I know is what the psychiatrists tell me."

"Fine," I said. "That's fine. What do they tell you?"

Seeing that I was really serious, Paul reached into a desk drawer and pulled out some memoranda.

"You understand," he began, "that we have no battle casualties of our own among ground personnel. A few have been sent up from North Africa, but so far, most of our hospital cases are Air Forces people."

"Even if you have no battle casualties, are you receiving any NP cases from your own troops?"

Paul shook his head. "Practically none."

"How about those from North Africa?" Ralph asked.

Again Paul consulted his memoranda.

"There are a few," he admitted.

"What per cent of the total?" Ralph persisted.

Paul did some rough calculations.

"According to these figures they amount to about twenty-five per cent."

"I don't call twenty-five per cent so few," Ralph opined.

I could see that Paul was getting slightly annoyed, so I cut in. "Are they all psychoneurotics, or do those figures include psychotics as well?"

Paul put down his papers and leaned forward; elbows propped, with chin in hands. "Are you inquiring into our figures or our diagnoses?" he demanded truculently.

"We're not questioning either one, Paul," I assured him. "But, for the record, we would like to know how many are really insane and how many come under each of the seven recognized categories of psychoneurosis."

Paul got up and carefully poured us each another portion of tea.

"Are you satisfied that the distinction between all varieties of psychiatric cases can be clearly defined?" he asked.

"Why do you ask that?" I inquired cautiously.

"Because," he responded tartly, slowly stirring his tea, "in adding up all mental cases sent in from the field we have found that, instead of the seven categories of psychoneurosis recognized by the War Department, our psychiatrists have improvised to a point where we now have about sixty-three."

"But there aren't that many categories," I protested.

Paul grinned. "But there are that many psychiatrists!"

"You mean each doctor uses different words for the same thing?"

"Not exactly," Paul sipped his tea. "Each one, however, is likely to mix them up or trade words around until, as I said, we found some sixty-three combinations."

"But they're all agreed that, regardless of category, the patients are psychoneurotics?"

"All but some of the flight surgeons down in Africa. They are beginning to diagnose their Air Corps casualties as 'battle fatigue,' and 'operational fatigue'."

"Are they psychoneurotic cases?"

"Well," Paul was a little guarded, "they give them the same treatment."

"Do they use pentothal and electro shock?"

"They use pentothal, all right, or else sodium amatol, which is pretty much the same thing. But I haven't heard about any electro-shock treatments. Have you?"

"We know they have been trying it out on psychotics," I said. "It is supposed to be better than the old method of using insulin to produce a state of coma."

"They may be using it in North Africa, then, but we aren't doing any of it here," said Paul, decisively.

"Well, we're trailing a bunch of constitutional psychopaths that were shipped to Africa," I said, "so we can find out about the rest of the psychiatric angles when we get there."

Paul stared at me in utter surprise. "What do you mean, a bunch of constitutional psychopaths?"

We explained our mission regarding the large group of men shipped out of the East Coast Processing Center. When we were done, Paul had a hearty laugh. "For a minute, you had me worried," he admitted.

"Why?" I asked, but Paul wouldn't tell. Suddenly, Ralph slapped his knee and exploded into one of his own merry laughs.

"I know what was bothering him," he pointed an accusing finger at Paul. "He probably shipped all his own constitutional psychopaths down there to get rid of them and thought we had caught him at it."

"You," Paul remarked, "can go to hell." But he said it good-naturedly.

I got to my feet and shook hands. "At least, we're going as far as Africa." I bade Paul good-bye and wished him luck. He wished us the same.

"How do we get to Africa?" asked Ralph as we walked down Park Lane toward the officers' club.

"The same way we got to the United Kingdom," I said. "By airplane."

Ralph looked across at Hyde Park where groups of people and lone couples walked or reclined upon the grass—some of them quite intimately.

"Don't you think there are a lot of things we should look into here, before we go?" he asked, hopefully.

"Well," I replied, "I don't suppose the Air Transport Command can set us up with a priority right away."

But that is where I got fooled. We were on a train returning to Glasgow the very next night.

"I suppose we should be flattered at how quickly they fixed us up to get out of here," I said when, at Prestwick, we found ourselves booked on the first plane out.

"You can be flattered if you want to be," retorted Ralph, "but I think they were just a little too eager to get rid of us."

"Maybe they put us in the same class with the constitutional psychopaths," I grinned.

"You ain't kidding!" retorted Ralph. "And I bet we stay in that category when we reach North Africa."

Whatever other classification might have been given us, we were still VIP's when, after a fourteen-hour night flight which detoured well out to sea to avoid enemy fighters, we landed at Marrakech. From the plane we were taken at once to a beautiful villa with luxurious beds and sunken tile bathtubs.

"Hope I don't catch trench foot around here," laughed Ralph, looking down at several heavy oriental rugs scattered around on the floor.

"If things don't get any worse than this," I said, "we'll probably manage to survive."

Conditions could hardly have gotten any better, but neither

did they get much worse. From Marrakech we went on to Casablanca, then Oran and finally to Algiers. There, our accommodations were of the best, although once again our hotel rooms looked directly across at a row of buildings half demolished by bombs.

But that did not bother us half as much as the thought of appearing at Allied Headquarters next morning and trying to explain why some three thousand men had been shipped to North Africa after having deserted their outfits to avoid the hazards of going overseas. We would have slept much better could we have foreseen the Supreme Commander's attitude in the matter.

The Chief of Staff, having served with both Ralph and me before the war, received us with very little formality.

"What the hell are you fellows doing over here?"

We explained as best we could about our interest in psychiatry and then about the shipment of men from the East Coast Processing Center.

When we had finished, Beetle fiddled around with some papers and then said without rancor, "Those were the only replacements we've received so far and they certainly were pretty poor material for the General to fight a war with."

Having no rebuttal we waited for Beetle to go on.

"We were all sore when the caliber of those men was discovered, because we are trying to win a war and it didn't look as though Washington was giving us much help. In fact, the General got on the phone and told them so. But when he found out all the circumstances surrounding that shipment, he agreed to take his fair share of such people in the future, provided they were sent over in smaller groups and not all at one time."

Ralph and I exchanged looks of relief. We certainly had not expected any such liberal and broadminded viewpoint on the matter as that. Returning my glance to Beetle, I found him regarding me with the unblinking stare of a watchful bulldog.

"What did you call those men, Cookie?" he asked crisply.

"Why--er," I was taken by surprise, "the doctors call them constitutional psychopaths, General."

He pushed a paper around his desk with one finger. "If a group of men, travelling in trucks from Oran to Algiers, shot off the insulators on all the telegraph poles and tied up our entire system of communications, just to be shooting at something, would you call them constitutional psychopaths?"

"I certainly would," I said with distinct disapproval. "Is that what those fellows did?"

Beetle shook his head. "It wasn't the men you were talking about. The ones who did that were from a crack airborne division." He pondered a moment and then asked, "How about a man who would offer to bet he could knock over two out of three Arabs working in a field, just to prove his marksmanship?"

Ralph and I both agreed that such action was sure proof of psychopathic tendencies.

"And a fellow who would chuck a hand grenade into a group of other American soldiers just for a practical joke?" Beetle questioned further.

We admitted that also was clearly in the field of psychiatry, whereupon Beetle grinned wryly.

"If that's the case," he said, "then there are a hell of a lot more constitutional psychopaths in this theater than the few you are looking for."

Ralph and I thought that over before I asked, "But what did become of the bunch we are looking for?"

"We sent them up as replacements to front-line units. What happened to them after that, I don't know." Beetle looked at both Ralph and me a little speculatively, I thought, before continuing. "All we're interested in is whether or not a man will fight! If he does, we let him get away with a lot more than if he won't."

"Then, those guys who shot at insulators and Arabs, and threw hand grenades at innocent by-standers were fighters?" asked Ralph eagerly.

"Some of the best!" agreed Beetle.

Ralph turned to me. "Hear that, Cookie? It means that constitutional psychopaths will fight!"

I wasn't entirely convinced. "It shows that fighting guys may pull some psychopathic stunts, all right, but it doesn't prove those constitutional gangplank-jumping psychopaths of ours are fighters, does it?"

I looked at Beetle inquiringly.

"There's one way of finding out," he stated.

"How's that?"

"Go ask their company commanders," he waved his hand vaguely eastward.

Ralph and I exchanged sheepish grins. "You bring a helmet and gas mask, Ralphie?"

"No, did you?"

"Don't worry," said Beetle, grimly, "you can pick up plenty at any salvage dump along the road." Then, just as we were leaving, he called, "If you fellows do find out what kind of guys will fight and which won't, let me know. The General would be interested."

Outside Allied Headquarters, Ralph and I paused to look out over Algiers and its harbor full of ships.

"So far, we don't seem to have learned very much," reflected Ralph.

"Oh, I don't know," I replied, breathing in the warm air, a welcome change from English fog. "We found out there have been sixty-three kinds of psychoneurotics instead of seven."

"Sixty-five," corrected Ralph, "don't forget the 'battle fatigue' and 'operational fatigue' that Paul told us about."

"That's right," I conceded, "we'll have to see where the difference is."

"Yeah! And we've also got to find out what the difference is between the constitutional psychopath who runs away from being made to fight and the fighter who turns out to be a constitutional psychopath."

We stood silent for awhile, contemplating the distant Mediterranean and the seemingly insoluble problem which was ours.

"Say," Ralph broke the spell of our momentary meditation, "are you going to let old Hy know, and Ossie up in London, that all is forgiven and to quit worrying about that shipment from the Processing Center?"

I looked at Ralph for a moment and then back to where dusty hills raised bare contours on the misty horizon.

"Let 'em fret," I said, "we are the ones to do the worrying."

"Why?" asked Ralph.

"Listen!" I said.

Faintly, from beyond those red, hazy hills came a broken, intermittent rumbling. It might have been thunder, only there was not a single cloud in that translucent Mediterranean sky.

"I'm afraid I know what you mean," Ralph said, and then essayed one of his habitual grins. "Where do you suppose one of those salvage dumps is that Beetle was telling us about?"

CHAPTER 8

GI PSYCHIATRY

~~~~~~

HILL 609 WAS HIGH, BLEAK AND DUSTY, THE KEY POINT of a horseshoelike ridge looking across a long sloping plain towards the town of Mateur, some ten miles to the northeast. The whole ridge was criss-crossed with old German trenches and pocked with more recently dug American foxholes.

The war had moved on beyond Mateur in the direction of Tunis, so the doughboys occupying Hill 609 and Hill 523 to the south were sitting on the edge of their private excavations, wandering about, or lying sprawled out in dejected sleep among the rocks and shrubs.

Ralph Bing and I each sat on a boulder, regarding a blond-headed young Infantry captain who sat cross-legged in front of a small cave hollowed out of the rocky soil.

"Here comes one of my lieutenants," said the captain, nodding his head toward the crest of the hill.

Down the slope came a tall lieutenant, with chin thrust slightly forward, and eyes appraising us suspiciously. "Brass," I could almost see him saying to himself. "Some more Brass snooping around." I would have bet money he wanted to spit, only in that barren land any form of moisture was too precious to part with, even in a gesture of disgust.

"Hello, Dave," an amused gleam was in the captain's bright blue eyes as he glanced from his lieutenant to Ralph and me. "Take a load off your feet."

We were introduced, as Dave's six feet of lanky frame were being folded into a position of ease. "They were asking me about those replacements we got a couple of months ago down at Bou Kadra," the captain concluded.

A heavy flush flooded Dave's bronzed features and I saw that he was several years younger than his company commander.

"What about 'em?" Dave asked, somewhat defiantly. When he spoke, cracks in his parched lips opened to show streaks of dust-caked blood.

"Well," I said, "we're interested in finding out what happened to them."

While talking, I had unhooked my canteen and unscrewed the top. Both Dave and the captain looked at me in horrified embarrassment for a moment, and then each gazed off in different directions. All water was on a strictly rationed basis in that area, and on a very meager basis at that. A man might have water and need some badly, but he wasn't supposed to show such poor taste as to take a drink in front of others who might not be so fortunate as to have any.

But I didn't have water. That morning I had been fortunate enough to obtain a bottle of wine and my canteen was full to the neck as I held it out invitingly to the captain. He accepted it with apologetic reluctance, but after one sniff of its contents an appreciative grin wrinkled his dust-covered face.

"We're being bribed, Dave," he chuckled, and took a couple of husky swallows. Then, after an inquiring glance at me, passed the canteen to his lieutenant. From then on our conversation was on a more friendly scale.

"Those replacements were a pain in the neck," said Dave, making a tentative try at moistening his sore lips with the tip of his tongue. "They were bodies to fill vacancies, but that's about all that could be said of 'em. We got them at Bou Kadra just before we made that end run around behind the Army for a surprise attack. Those fellows didn't cause us any trouble then, because the chow was good and we weren't under fire."

Dave paused and looked at his company commander for confirmation.

"That's right," the captain agreed, "but first tell them about Peterson."

Dave grinned sheepishly and went through the motions of inspecting the soles of his shoes to cover his embarrassment.

"Well, he said, "Peterson was one of those fellows who couldn't do anything. I remember how, in physical training periods, he couldn't even play leap-frog. He'd kick the other guy or fall on his face. I took him out alone and worked with him, but he never got anywhere!"

Dave looked up as though half expecting Ralph and me to doubt his word. But both of us had commanded companies and in every outfit we had ever been in charge of there had been at least one Peterson. Our understanding smiles reassured Dave, so he continued.

"It wasn't so much that Peterson couldn't ever do anything the right way, but he was always doing something the wrong way. At inspections he never had all his equipment and at reviews he was never in step. There didn't ever seem to be a day that I wasn't on the carpet on account of Peterson. So a couple of weeks before we left the States I took our regimental medico out and bought him a few drinks."

Noting the reminiscent faraway look dawning in Dave's eyes, I hastily proffered my canteen. When it had gone the rounds, Dave resumed.

"The medico sent Peterson off somewhere and we sailed without him. And then, at Bou Kadra, when we needed battle replacements in the worst way, who shows up with a lot of other misfits, but Peterson!"

Dave looked up at the captain and their eyes fought a silent battle. "Go on," challenged the captain. "Tell 'em that you had the first platoon when you got rid of Peterson, and when he came back you had the third platoon, but I made you take him just the same!"

Before Dave could answer, Ralph pulled out a package of cigarettes and extended the opened end. "How about a smoke?" he offered, one eyelid dropping slightly for my benefit. When each had taken one, Ralph pressed the whole pack upon the captain. "Go on, take it," Ralph insisted. "We can get some more."

Without appearing to be rude, I could see the captain trying to ascertain how many cigarettes were left and mentally calculating just how he was going to divide them up among his command.

Under cover of Ralph's diversion, I asked, "What eventually happened to Peterson?"

"Oh," Dave drew smoke deeply into his lungs. "He did just like always. The very first thing, he stuck his head up when everyone else had theirs down and a German sniper put a bullet right through the middle of it!"

Ralph and I were a little taken aback and watched silently as Dave carefully rubbed out his cigarette on a nearby rock and dropped the butt into his pocket.

"Did you get all those guys into the front line?" asked Ralph, interestedly.

"I only had about three others," Dave said, a little morosely. "One of them was a guy named Perkowski. He always was a dead beat and ran away just before we got to the Port of Embarkation. When he rejoined at Bou Kadra he had some kind of an excuse and since he was better than nothing, I guess we were glad to have him." Dave shook his head gloomily. "But that was a mistake. When we moved to Beja everyone knew we were going into a fight. So Perkowski volunteered to go back to the kitchen to bring up chow and that's the last time I saw him!"

"What happened?" I asked.

Dave picked up a rock and heaved it at a venturesome lizard some ten feet away. "The next I heard of Perkowski was in a letter from headquarters asking why I hadn't recommended Private Perkowski for a Purple Heart on account of he's in a hospital with a bullet hole through his foot!"

"What did you tell them?" grinned Ralph.

"*I* told them!" interposed the captain, grimly. "I said we had plenty of guys getting shot where it counted, without wasting a Purple Heart on anyone who got himself wounded at a ration dump five miles beyond range of enemy artillery. If I ever see Perkowski wearing a Purple Heart, I'll choke him to death with my bare hands!"

"He will be wearing it, don't you worry," Dave laughed bitterly. "Just like somebody will be spending Peterson's ten thousand dollars insurance. The government sure would have been better off if they'd taken my advice and gotten rid of that dumb cluck instead of spending ten grand, just to have him bumped off!"

"What happened to the rest of those replacements you got at Bou Kadra?" I asked.

"Well," reflected the captain, "there was that fellow Gustane. He was always using big words to tell about the rights of men and how they were being trampled on. But I noticed the only thing Gustane was really interested in was his own skin. The boys caught him stealing water from the company supply and they would have killed him if I hadn't interfered. So I put him on kitchen police, and the first thing he does is swipe our kitchen truck one night to go off on a joyride of his own, runs into a mine crater and busts our truck all to hell. For that, the mess sergeant kicked his tail over half of North Africa and we haven't seen Mr. Gustane since!"

The captain shifted slightly to glance searchingly over the hillside where his men drowsed in the sun, for all the world like a colony of prairie dogs, ready at the first sign of danger to whisk into their holes.

"Some of those sadsacks may be around right now," he resumed, "but if they are, it's only because we aren't in a fight. Give us movement orders and let us start up to the front and those birds would be hidden out so quick it would take a regiment of MPs to find 'em!"

"Tell me something," I said, earnestly. "What do your other kids think of those gangplank jumpers and hider-outers?"

Both young officers inspected us with careful scrutiny. Satisfied, apparently, that we were versed in something other than purely theoretical warfare, the captain settled the seat of his pants a little more firmly on the rocky terrain and began to expound.

"In our first scrap all of us were eager beavers. We'd run a mile to get a shot at the Krauts and for a lot of the boys it was their last mile. From then on we were more cautious. We lost fewer men but we had losses just the same. Taking this hill right here, we had fifty per cent casualties. So now we all know that each time we go in our own number gets that much closer."

The captain scooped up a handful of pebbles and began tossing them at a crack in a large boulder.

"It's nice to be a hero if you live to enjoy it," he resumed.

"But our boys are beginning to wonder where the hell the rest of our Army is. We aren't anxious to win all the medals. And each time we go into a fight, a few more of the conscientious lads begin to wonder just how wrong it is to hide out and not go forward with the outfit. So the way it works out is, the more fighting a guy does, the more he knows how to keep from getting killed foolishly. And the first thing you know he figures out it's foolish to get killed at all. From then on he's not so sure the dead beats haven't been just a little smarter than he has been all the time."

The captain threw his last pebble, dusted off his hands and crossed his arms. "It's all very much mixed up," he admitted. "Some folks won't fight at all, others will fight a little bit and still others will stay with it until they drop or go crazy. And I'm damned if I know what makes any of them tick the way they do!"

I got to my feet a little stiffly and placed my hand on his shoulder. "Captain," I said, "you've got enough to do without worrying about such matters. Just keep yourself alive and maybe you can help figure it out when the war is over."

Ralph and I shook hands and wished the captain and Dave the best of luck, before starting down the rocky hill to where our car was hidden in an olive grove. We glanced curiously at the young Americans we passed on the way, wondering which were fighters and which were not. They all looked the same. At the bottom of the hill we found the driver of our car in conversation with a motorcycle MP.

"Anything wrong?" I asked.

"No, I guess not," the MP looked us over quite carefully. "But I have to check up on all cars and trucks in this area. The boys are kind of careless whose car they use these days and what they use 'em for. When I came along your driver was off in the bushes somewhere and your car wasn't being watched. It wouldn't have stayed here long."

I interrupted the driver's explanation of the necessity that took him away from the car to ask a question of the MP. "You think someone would have stolen our car?"

A dry grin overspread the MP's face. "It ain't exactly stealing; it's more like borrowing, or converting it to some other use. But you leave any kind of an automobile standing around with nobody watching it and the boys are going to start salvaging parts or just take the whole thing along to save time."

"How long have you been on MP duty?" Ralph asked idly.

"Ever since I came in the Army. And before that I was a cop for six years. I guess that's why they made me an MP."

"Say, tell me," Ralph's interest quickened, "do you think the constitutional psychopath, that is to say, the more or less criminal type or morally weak person can be made into a good soldier?"

"Listen, colonel," the MP regarded Ralph very seriously, "if a man's a crook in Chicago, he's going to be crooked in New York, Cincinnati, or anywhere else you put him. And that goes for the Army, too. What you've got in the Army is people, and in any bunch of people you're going to have a given amount of crooks and weaklings."

"Then you don't think the Army can make men out of them?" I asked, both amused and pleased to find a cop who was also a philosopher.

"You give them men's jobs, all right," he conceded, "and maybe you can make them do those jobs for a while. But there ain't many of them you can change inside. They'll go back, sooner or later, to what they was in the first place."

"Well, look, said Ralph eagerly, "how about these fellows who take cars and things like that? They're soldiers and most of them are darn good fighters, too."

"Sure," the MP agreed, "and they do lots of things that would get them in jail back home. But they do it just for the hell of it like fellows go off on a spree and do crazy things. They ain't like the regular drunk who never sobers up and will do most anything to get more liquor. You take all this shooting now," the MP warmed up to his subject, "when the war's over these guys ain't going to keep on looking for someone to kill. Chances are most of them won't ever want to see another dead man or fire another gun."

"Perhaps you're right," I said and then added experimentally, "Have you had any experience with psychoneurotics?"

To my surprise the MP took that one right in his stride. "Oh, sure! We pick up a lot of stragglers that the medicos call psychoneurotics. But they ain't much different from the other kind we been talking about. They never had what it takes to begin with, so they cave in as soon as the goin' gets tough."

"Well, much obliged," I said, getting into the automobile. "Next time we won't be so careless with our car."

The MP nodded, straddled his motorcycle and shoved down the starting pedal. "And you'd better not go wandering around like you done, either," he admonished our driver. "First thing you know you'll step on a mine and then you'll be needin' spare parts for yourself." With that parting shot he roared off down the road.

"That's a cop for you," laughed Ralph. But our driver called him something else, under his breath. Then, catching my eye in the windshield mirror, he said hastily, "Where to, sir?"

I took out a list, together with an operations map on which

were marked the locations of various headquarters. "That seems to have been the last company commander we set out to see, Ralph."

"Well, they've all told us the same kind of stories," Ralph replied. "Why don't we try some of the boys higher up?"

We consulted our map. There's a regimental CP in that farmhouse a couple of miles down this road." Ralph put his finger on a mark. "Let's drive there and see who's in it."

Just before reaching the farmhouse, we were halted by another MP and told that we would have to leave our car under cover of some trees and go the rest of the way on foot. It wasn't healthy in North Africa to have too many tire tracks leading to a headquarters. So Ralph and I got out and walked.

Inside the farmhouse we found a deceptively indulgent-looking colonel chewing gum who had been a still more deceptively indulgent looking captain chewing gum the last time we had seen him in prewar days. "Well I'll be crucified," he said, with a drawl as long as the State of Illinois itself. "Will you look at who's here! Is the war over or have you guys lost your way?"

"Darned if it isn't two-goal George, the demon polo player," Ralph jeered in return. "What did they bring you over for, to teach equitation?"

After those and a few other more ribald pleasantries we settled down to business.

"Look, George," I said, "we are making inquiry into what happened to a bunch of replacements sent over here about the time your outfit was at Bou Kadra. Do you remember them?"

"Are you trying to pull my leg?" Despite George's drawl the rising crescendo of his voice resembled greatly the approach of an 88 shell. "Of course I remember them. I dream about them. Every day I'm trying to get some of them out of my hair. There never was a worse bunch of misfitting, misbegotten lumps of humanity. If that's the best you have left, keep 'em home and we'll win the war without any help. If I could get my hands on the guy who sent that load of tripe over here, I'd crucify him."

"They were better than nothing at all, weren't they, George?" Ralph chided gently.

"Not much!" George remained vehement, "Not much at all! I bet I could go out and get a bunch of volunteer boy scouts who'd do a lot better."

"What do those fellows do that's so bad?" I asked.

"You name it and they'll do it," replied George bitterly. "If a captured gun goes off accidentally and hurts any of our own men, it's one of those replacements who didn't know it was loaded. When a ration truck hits a mine and our chow gets blown to hell, it's one of those same replacements we can thank for going hungry. Anytime my AWOL rate starts climbing I know my noncoms have forgotten to keep a close watch on those birds and the medicos taking sick report know them all by their first names."

Ralph and I pricked up our ears at that last statement.

"Have you been having many psychiatric casualties, George?" I asked, as casually as I could.

George opened his mouth and then shut it again in complete surprise. "Say," his drawl was more prolonged with suspicion. "Are you fellows mixed up in those newfangled ideas the Medical Corps is trying to put over on us?"

"What ideas are those, George?" smiled Ralph.

"There's a medical colonel visiting the division who is trying to tell us that some of the guys who fold up without getting hit are sick, or something. Believe me, if I catch anyone trying to tell my men they are sick when they're just trying to lie down on the job, I'll crucify him! Why, Goddammit, they can't do that!"

"Those men are probably suffering from an anxiety state," said Ralph, nodding sagely at me for George's benefit.

"No doubt," I agreed, solemnly, "and the colonel, of course, is some noted neuropsychiatrist. He's probably down here making a study of psychoneurotics and constitutional psychopaths."

Alarmed, George looked from me to Ralph and back again. "Now listen," he recovered himself, "I don't know what you fellows are up to, but you can't fool me about my own men. They aren't any crazier than you are and I don't want any nut doctors coming around saying they are."

"They're not crazy at all, George," I said, cutting out the horseplay. "The ones we are talking about, the psychoneurotics, *are* sick. They have functional disorders induced by nervous strain under stress."

"What kind of disorders?" demanded George.

"Why, they lose their appetite, develop headaches, or are constantly tired and depressed. Some of them have insomnia or, when they do go to sleep, they have horrible nightmares. They get jittery and are too sick to carry on."

"What are you trying to give me?" George snorted in disgust. "Who doesn't lose his appetite just before going into a scrap? And who isn't jittery and who doesn't have nightmares after being in one? We're all like that, only it doesn't mean we are sick."

"The difference is, George, that you get over it in a very short time and are back to normal again. Some of the others don't. They're the same a month after a scrap as the day after, and they are still that way when it comes time to go into the next fight. They never recover from their anxiety and it gets steadily worse as long as they are under the conditions that first made them that way. That is why they are sick and called psychoneurotics."

"Nuts!" George drawled. "I don't believe it. Somebody has thought up a new two-bit word for being yellow!"

Ralph and I regarded George thoughtfully. Here was a fighting guy and his opinion carried considerable weight.

"George, do you have a regimental surgeon?" asked Ralph.

"Sure, and a damn good one, too. He's right here in the back room. You want to see him?"

"Why not bring him in here and we'll all talk to him?" I suggested.

In response to George's shouted summons, a dumpy little major, with a blond mustache and beat-up spectacles trotted into the room.

"Charlie," George began, without any preamble, "how many men from this outfit have dead-beat their way into a hospital?"

Charlie's eyes bulged a little behind the scratched-up lenses of his glasses and he wet his lips nervously before answering. "Why, Colonel," he defended, "I don't think there have been any real dead-beats sent to a hospital."

"Probably not," Ralph spoke up, "but have all of them been wounded?"

"Why no, of course not!" Charlie responded, with more assurance. Evidently, the slight apprehension displayed in dealing with his regimental commander was not felt when speaking to others. "We've had our share of pulmonary trouble, malaria, trench feet and so on, just like all other organizations."

"How about psychoneurosis?" I asked, quietly. "Have you written that diagnosis on any of your hospital tags?"

The major's rotund little body jerked once, spasmodically, as though a hyperdermic needle had unexpectedly been jabbed into one of his round little buttocks. His eyes rolled appealingly from us to his natural protector, the colonel.

"Now, Goddammit, you can't do that," George immediately intervened between us and his subordinate. "We're fighting a war and we're not getting much help doing it, either. You're no doctors and Charlie is. You leave him and his diagnoses alone."

George's sudden belligerence, coupled with Charlie's obvious relief, struck Ralph and me as being so funny we could not restrain our laughter.

"Listen, George," I said, when we had recovered from our merriment, "this inquiry is not on the critical side at all. We're honestly looking for information. So, come on and relax. Just what is the deal regarding these birds who filter back to the first aid stations with no visible signs of sickness or wounds?"

George regarded us fixedly for a few moments, while his habitual gum-chewing became more deliberate and serious. "All right," he finally said, "you asked for it and now you're going to get it! To start out with, I want to say that anybody who thinks our boys want to fight, is crazy. And anyone who believes they will keep on fighting indefinitely, hasn't got the brains that God gave geese. So it comes down to how long we humanly can keep them going while they are in danger of being killed. For that, I turn you over to Charlie who sees them all and has some idea of what their limitations are."

At this display of confidence, the chubby little doctor lost all signs of self-consciousness and uncertainty. All of a sudden, he became dignified and assured. He was in his own element and possessed knowledge he knew to be irrefutable. Consequently, he balanced back and forth on the balls of his feet and one could almost visualize him as addressing a group of internes.

"I am not a psychiatrist," he began simply, "but any doctor in a combat regiment soon discovers that his most difficult problems are in the fields of psychiatry and psychology. During training we had to deal with those men who didn't want to be in the Army, at all. Later we encountered those who were determined to avoid hazardous duty, regardless of consequences. Now, we are confronted with men who are beginning to lose that fortitude which permitted them to endure the nightmares of battle."

"Are there many of them?" I interrupted.

A sad shadow of a smile flickered across the little doctor's face. "Few of them were ever mentally prepared for such an ordeal. Their own pride and sense of obligation to their comrades keep them going. When those fail, they come to me, exhausted, both in body and mental attributes. First, they must be restored physically. I give them nourishing food and then an opiate for dreamless rest. After that, I work on them mentally."

Charlie glanced down apologetically at his none too impressive figure. "I don't look much like a soldier and they wouldn't listen to me a minute if I tried to make the eagle scream or talked about honor or duty or what we are fighting for. The only possible approach to their restoration is along the lines of loyalty to their squad, the platoon, and the company. In other words, the 'outfit'."

"How about loyalty to their officers?" asked Ralph, with a wicked grin at George.

Charlie shook his head. "Officers are part of the 'outfit' if they are liked. Otherwise they are outsiders and the men have no feeling of loyalty towards them, whatever. Usually, however, we are able to return a man to his organization the first time. But if he is not killed or wounded he will come back and at each appearance our mental therapy is less effective. Sooner or later we will have extracted the last ounce of performance we are ever going to get out of the man and he is through!"

"Do you mean he is through with combat, or with the Army, or what?" I asked earnestly.

Charlie shrugged, "He definitely is through with combat. And as long as he remains in the Army he will always retain the fear that something will happen to again force him into battle. Therefore, he has but one thought and desire and that is to get out of the Army entirely so he never again will be exposed to the many kinds of violent death he has seen and cannot obliterate from his every thought!"

In the momentary silence that followed, Ralph spoke up, "Does that make him a psychoneurotic or not?"

Charlie removed his battered spectacles, rubbed their lenses vigorously and replacing them on his nose, regarded Ralph reproachfully. "All I know is, that if I were to write down the symptoms of those men, they would correspond exactly to those of a depressive or anxiety type of psychoneurotic. Of course, a psychoneurotic's symptoms theoretically date back to something in early life which influences or controls his reflexes and actions later on. But these men's reflections are directly and irrevocably associated with their experiences in battle. Therefore, since they never before had been subjected to a comparable experience, it is difficult to establish beyond reasonable doubt an explanation of their reaction to the greatest stress that any person can be subjected to."

For a little guy, Charlie had certainly done well by a large subject, as Ralph and I both told him. "You'd make a darn good psychiatrist," I assured him.

Charlie shot a timorous glance at his colonel while extracting a folded paper from his shirt pocket. "Thanks very much," he said, "I'm glad you think so, because I've just received orders directing my return to England for a course in psychiatry."

"What!" George nearly swallowed his gum. "When did that come in?" He snatched the order from Charlie's hand and glanced angrily at the authenticating signature. "Why it's a Division order," he said in amazement. "What do you suppose has gotten into those guys? Our medicos have been doing all right. They've been taking care of the sick and wounded during this whole campaign. What more could they learn in school?"

"Perhaps they haven't all been doing so well as Charlie has with your battle fatigue or psychiatric cases," I suggested. "Maybe some of the men have been forced to stay in too long."

"Well, for Pete's sake," George almost shouted, "how else are you going to run a war; let all the guys go who don't want to fight?"

"As to that, I wouldn't know," I shrugged and got to my feet.

"Your division commander, who signed Charlie's orders, may have some information on the subject. At any rate, I intend to ask him about it."

"Well, when you see Jerry, you tell him for me that if he has any ideas about making it easier for men to get into hospitals instead of the front lines, he is going to be awful short of soldiers pretty soon."

"We'll tell him his division might lose its reputation," agreed Ralph as we shook hands and started from the farmhouse towards our car. "That is, if it has one to lose!"

"Why, Goddammit," George yelled after us, "this is the best division in the whole Army and you know it."

Ralph was a little thoughtful as we trudged through the rocks and sand to where our car and driver were waiting. "This *is* one of the best divisions in the Army," he soliloquized. "Do you suppose we should have picked some other division to work on?"

"No!" I said. "That is why I chose this organization. It has the longest history and finest record in the Army. No matter what we find out, the people at home can't ever say we went around looking for the worst."

With the toe of one shoe, Ralph dribbled a round pebble ahead of him for a few steps. "Do you think the folks back Stateside are going to believe us anyhow?" he asked.

"Not if we intimate that their boys are anything but natural born heroes," I answered.

"Then where do these psychoneurotics fit in?" demanded Ralph.

"That," I sighed drearily, "is what we still have to find out."

CHAPTER 9

GIDEON'S THREE HUNDRED MEN

~~~~~~

And the Lord said unto Gideon, "By the three hundred men that lapped will I save you, and deliver the Midianites into thine hand; and let all the other people go every man unto his place."—Judges VII, 7.

THE CAR CARRYING RALPH BING AND ME GLIDED OVER one of the longest concrete spans in North Africa, swerved down between mud walls and then along the winding, uneven streets of Beja. Following an MP escort we arrived at a converted French dwelling, housing division headquarters. The general commanding had served in the same division as I had during World War I, and his greeting was both friendly and cordial.

"I'd have been glad to see you anyhow, Cookie," he said, "but if you can help me in this business of psychoneurosis I hear you're working on, I'll be more than grateful."

He led us into a large room with maps pinned on the wall and offered us comfortable chairs.

"You been having trouble with psychoneurotics?" I asked, looking him over with interest. Jerry had always been on the dashing, harum-scarum side, but now he appeared grave and worried.

"It isn't so much trouble as it is something I'm not sure I understand. In the last war we heard a lot about "shell shock" but you remember we didn't take it seriously. When the men referred to anyone being that way they just meant he was sort of goofy or something.

"Well, when all this talk of psychoneurosis started I didn't pay much attention to it. I just gave orders that anyone showing up at a first-aid station or hospital without a wound or serious illness was to be run right back into the front line again and it wouldn't bother me a bit if an inch or so of cold steel was applied to their rear ends as a reminder to stay there!"

Ralph and I exchanged rueful glances. Here was the same attitude we had encountered in Jimmy-the-Hard and other division commanders during the training periods back home. Unaware of the pattern he was following, Jerry continued. "I couldn't believe there was anything to this idea of men getting sick from fear until a sergeant was brought to me the other day who just stated flatly that he couldn't go back and see any more of his buddies getting killed."

Jerry shook his head. "That sergeant was as good a soldier as any in this division and I have personally pinned two decorations on him before he cracked up. But he just sat here and cried. He said he didn't care what we did with him but he wasn't going back!"

Jerry got up and walked nervously about the room. "Teddy," referring to his assistant division commander, "and my G-1 think we should make an example of that sergeant before any more men get the same crazy idea." Jerry halted and I could see he was appealing to me for advice.

"What does your division surgeon say about the case?" I asked.

Jerry shrugged. "He feels that the man should be sent to a hospital for observation and treatment."

"And you don't want to take his advice?"

"It's not that, Cookie," Jerry sounded almost plaintive. "There's something more than just this case. I'm afraid if I let down once there will be a lot more. Yet, at the same time, my surgeon has just about convinced me that there is a great deal more to this business than I know about!"

"How would it be if we talked to your surgeon?" I suggested.

"Certainly. Do you want me to be present or shall I leave?"

"We want you to stay, of course. We'd like to have Teddy and your G-1 in on it, too, if you don't mind."

"Hell, no!" Jerry relievedly called for all three officers. "If you give us a straight steer on this you can have anything in the division."

Of the three officers who joined us, Teddy was the only one Ralph and I had known previously. He was a little below medium height and, although quiet-spoken, a proven ball of fire in action. G-1 was a stocky lad whose accent and mode of speech easily identified him as coming from the Lone-Star State of Texas. The freckled-faced, red-headed surgeon was called Dan and must have played havoc with the nurses when an interne.

"We were discussing the Bright case," Jerry explained to them.

Teddy shrugged, as though such a discussion were hardly worthwhile. The G-1 was less moderate. "The only thing for that guy is a court-martial. What else could the man expect after refusing to go back in and fight?"

I looked at Dan, but he maintained a tight-lipped silence. Therefore, I asked him a direct question, "Does the sergeant have any functional disorders?"

"A marked traumatic tremor," he replied briefly.

"Do you classify his as an anxiety type, severe depressive, or what?"

A little of the reticence disappeared from Dan's attitude. "I haven't attempted to classify him. But I did ask Colonel Benson, who is a psychiatrist, to talk with Sergeant Bright and give me a diagnosis."

The G-1 opened his mouth to speak but I held up a detaining hand. "Doesn't the sergeant display any anxiety over what may happen to him by refusing to return to the front?"

"That's the strange part of it," there was a gleam of professional interest in Dan's eyes. "Apparently, he had decided that nothing we can do to him would be worse than going back so he appears quite relieved."

"What did Colonel Benson, the psychiatrist who saw the man, say?"

"He said that he had not a sufficient period of observation to complete a diagnosis but that, in his opinion, the sergeant was definitely psychoneurotic and if he were returned to the front he would suffer a complete breakdown."

"Wouldn't that be too bad?" G-1 drawled, unable to contain himself any longer. Teddy smiled his quiet agreement with G-1 but Jerry watched me inquiringly, so I ignored the interruption.

"If the sergeant is a psychoneurotic now, then he was one before he ever went into battle, wasn't he?"

"Presumably," replied Dan.

"But he fought just the same?" I persisted.

"He has twice been decorated for bravery!"

I caught an urgent signal from Ralph. Evidently he had some hot idea he was juggling about in his mind so I nodded for him to get rid of it.

"Colonel," he began, "in the Air Corps they have a system whereby a man flies a given number of missions and then is sent home for a rest. Is that right?"

"I believe that is correct," Dan replied.

"But on the ground there isn't any limit to the number of times a man must return to the front, is there?"

"None that I know of!"

"The only finish he sees is for the war to end or else to be either killed or seriously wounded?"

"Yes. "

"You've seen plenty of wounded, many of them so badly they know they can never be returned to the front. What has been their attitude?"

Dan regarded Ralph thoughtfully. "I see what you are getting at. When not suffering pain, those men are greatly relieved. Their morale is high."

"Isn't that about the way Sergeant Bright feels now?" Ralph grinned triumphantly.

Dan smiled slightly in response. "I wouldn't be surprised if it were."

"Well, I bet a court-martial will soon make him feel differently," G-1 blurted.

"Sure," Ralph turned on some sarcasm, "put him in jail where he'd be safe for the duration. Would that do you any good?"

"He could serve his time in the front lines with a suspended sentence," G-1 retorted. Teddy nodded and Jerry looked uncertain.

"Jerry," I said, "don't you suppose that everyone in the sergeant's outfit knows by now that he has cracked up?"

"In his, and a lot of other outfits, too," he agreed, a little sadly.

"Then you know that none of them would ever trust their lives to him or want him around. And he wouldn't be any good if he was. So, what would you gain by sending him back?"

Tapping out a cigarette and leaning forward, Teddy spoke for the first time. "On the other hand, what would we lose? How would the rest of the division react if we let a malingerer like that sergeant evade hazardous duty and still escape punishment?"

I heaved an inward sigh. Teddy, the personification of courage, would never understand any compromise regarding the lack of that attribute in others. The trouble was, they weren't all like Teddy.

"Let me put it this way," I attempted to explain. "You either believe in psychiatry or you don't. When a psychiatrist tells you a soldier is suffering from a severe neurosis he means the man is sick. If another doctor told you a man was suffering from a disease you were familiar with you would not question his decision to send that man to a hospital. But, if a psychiatrist tells you a man is sick and you do not believe there is any such sickness as the psychiatrist describes, you think the patient is malingering and the doctor is either crazy or some sort of a road block to the war effort!"

When I paused for breath, Teddy asked blandly, "So what?"

"Well," I pursued my theme, "those psychiatrists took a complete course in medicine the same as any other doctor and, in addition, spent several years studying under other recognized psychiatrists before being accepted as one themselves."

"Not now, they're not," G-1 contradicted. "They're sending some of our regular doctors to school for a few months and then calling them psychiatrists!"

"What of it?" I asked impatiently. "The same thing is done with line officers. A doughboy, an artilleryman or anyone else attends some specialist's school for a quick emergency course in some subject and comes out an expert. Where's the difference?"

That silenced G-1 for the moment because he knew as well as I did that many a line officer had successfully performed some specialist job, with very little previous training. Jerry knew it too, because he asked, "Then you believe that any doctor, after a few months' special course could distinguish between a malingerer and one of these fellows you call a psychoneurotic?"

"I think, as far as that goes, they could do it as well as a regular psychiatrist."

"Yeah!" said G-1, "But do the psychiatrists know what they're talking about? Particularly in a case like Sergeant Bright?"

"Colonel," I said, shaking my head, "don't think any of them claim to know all there is about this subject, because it is pretty big and comparatively new. But you can be sure of one thing, the psychiatrists are bound by their Hippocratic oath, the same as any other doctor. It is their duty to save the lives and sanity of human beings. What they recommend may seem bad for military discipline in some cases, but take my word for their recommendations being sincere. They believe in psychiatry, whether you do or not!"

The solemnity of my dissertation was somewhat marred by Teddy who, with a wink at G-1, leaned over confidentially to nudge Ralph, and with a nod of the head in my direction, said, *sotto voce,* "Pompous bastard, isn't he?"

"Nuts," I retored amidst the ensuing laughter, "all I'm trying to say is that you'll get into less trouble listening to your psychiatrists than you will disregarding their advice!"

Jerry nodded gravely. "I think you've got something Cookie," he said. "Anyhow, I'm going to take your advice."

Ralph and I got up, pleased at the thought of having been of some help. But our complacency was jarred when Teddy, in bidding us a smiling goodbye, remarked, "I still don't believe it!"

I disregarded that crack and reached over to shake hands with Dan. "Who is this Colonel Benson you were talking about?"

His freckles lit up appreciatively. " 'Freddy-the-Phantom' some of the boys call him. If he's not down in the front lines trying to find out what makes GI Joe nervous, he's probably back at GHQ giving brass hats the jitters."

"That, I would like to see," I admitted and turned to smile at Jerry. "I don't know whether we've been a help or a hindrance, but we mean well."

"Don't worry about that," he extended a hand to both Ralph and me. "We all do the best we can. I hope you find the answers you're looking for."

We thanked Jerry and proceeded to our car. The driver was talking to another GI who fell back as we came up. Along with a very smart salute, he cast a wistful glance at the empty front seat.

"Were you going our way?" I smiled.

It took him a minute to catch his breath. "Yes, sir! That is, if you're going to Algiers. I've got a five-day pass. Of course, there'll be a truck going that way . . ."

"Get in," I invited and the lad was happily seated almost as soon as the words were out of my mouth.

Ralph threw me a grateful look. There was nothing Ralph liked better than the chance to talk to a good, clean kid in uniform, and this boy really sparkled. "What's your name, soldier?" Ralph asked.

"Green, sir. Corporal Robert Green," and he told us his organization.

"That's a fine outfit," Ralph said, sincerely "How did you happen to get a five-day pass?"

Corporal Robert Green blushed. It started at his collar and spread like a rising tide over neck and face. He looked down at his feet. "I was lucky," he stated.

"How, lucky?" Ralph persisted. "You win it in a crap game?"

"Aw, no sir," Corporal Green looked back over his shoulder reproachfully. "Division needed a prisoner for information and offered a pass to anyone who brought one in. I took out a patrol the other night and ran into a couple of Krauts. That's how I was lucky." He drew out a letter from one pocket. "I've got a brother somewhere around Algiers, and I'm hopin' to find him."

I made mental note that the brother should be found. "Were you scared the night you ran into the Germans?"

He showed me a double row of even white teeth. "Yes, sir, I was scared all right! Anybody tells you he isn't scared up front is just a plain liar."

I nodded agreement. "Some of them get so scared they pull out, don't they?"

The corporal shifted uncomfortably in his seat, "Well, the fellows talk about that a lot, but it's mostly hot air. Not many of them could run out on the gang, even if they wanted to. Their pride wouldn't let them."

"Some of them do, though," I said. "A lot of them never even get up to the front line."

"Oh, them!" The corporal dismissed such personnel disdainfully. "They never get anywhere. Always bitchin' about everything. They don't belong to anything! They're just out for themselves."

Ralph and I exchanged startled looks. Out of the mouths of babes . . . "Lookie," Ralph took up the conversation, "some of the other fellows crack up too." He did not mention Sergeant Bright, but we were both thinking of him.

"Yeah, that's right," Corporal Green acknowledged. "Some of them do. But you can see it comin' on, and sometimes the other guys can help out."

"How do you mean, you can see it coming on?" I asked.

"Why, first they get trigger happy," the corporal explained. "They go running all over the place lookin' for something to shoot at. Then, the next thing you know they got the battle jitters. They jump if you light a match and go diving for cover if someone bounces a tin hat off a rock. Any kind of a sudden noise and you can just about see them let out a mental scream to themselves. When they get that way, you might just as well cross them off the roster because they aren't going to be any more use to the outfit."

"How can the other fellows help out in a case like that?" I inquired.

The corporal looked down at his hands a little sheepishly. "Aw, you can kind of cover up for a guy like that before he's completely gone. He can be sent back to get ammo or something. You know and he knows he's gonna stay out of sight for a while, but you don't let on, see? Then, he can pretend to himself he's got a reason for being back there and he still has his pride. Maybe he even gets his nerve back for the next time. But if he ever admits openly that he's runnin' away, he's through! After that, he's not ashamed any more, and he won't ever go back!"

I regarded that young corporal with some amazement and considerable respect. "How old are you?" I asked.

"Aw," the blush again seeped up from his collar, "I'm almost twenty!"

After that we talked of other things. When the car finally arrived in Algiers and the corporal wanted to thank us for the ride, we assured him that he had more than earned his passage. I gave him a scribbled note to one of my friends at headquarters and said, "Take this over to G-1 and they will help you find your brother." That done, Ralph and I sought out the office of the Theater Surgeon.

Fortunately, we found Colonel Benson, or Freddy, as Dan had called him, present at the headquarters instead of down somewhere wandering around in the front lines, as seemed to be his usual custom.

"Tell me," I said, when we had presented credentials and explained our mission, "how much do the people over here actually know about psychiatry?"

"If you mean me, I'm not bragging," he answered, cheerfully, "and if you mean all the others, they don't even know that much. We left the States before a psychiatrist was included in the tables of organization. Consequently, the commanders and most of their unit surgeons think we are here to condone cowardice and to get malingerers out of jail."

That certainly was laying it on the line, and our respect for Freddy increased materially. However, Ralph and I were there to be convinced, so I asked, "Well, are they correct?"

Freddy was unperturbed by my cynicism. "You might think so," he answered, "if you didn't know the difference between persons who *are* sick and those who just want to be sick!"

"Since we don't," Ralph grinned, engagingly, "how do we go about finding out?"

Freddy picked up an imposing looking paper from a nearby

desk and held it out for our scrutiny. "You start in by looking at figures like these." With a pencil he indicated some totals.

"During the first real engagement in this theater, a so-called National Guard division was teamed up with what was known as a Regular Army division. Actually, there was little, if any, difference in the type of personnel since both were filled with the products of Selective Service. However, the men in the Guard division were considerably awed by the history and prestige of the regular division and, following that particular engagement, hospital records indicate a ratio of psychiatric cases of about three for the Guard division as compared to one for the Regulars, and they all came from the same original source!"

Ralph and I went into a visual huddle. What Freddy had told us was entirely logical according to our lights, yet, at the same time, we detected in his method of presentation something equivalent to a slight-of-hand artist about to pull a rabbit, or even a Ford automobile, out of a hat. So, in mutual acquiescence we reserved judgment until after his act was completed.

"In the next fight," Freddy continued, seeing that we had no comment to offer, "that same Guard division was brigaded with another division from an adjacent State back home, with which there had always been a traditional rivalry as far back as World War I. And, strange to relate, when the smoke cleared away after that engagement, neither of those divisions had suffered enough psychiatric casualties to fill the cots of a single evacuation hospital!"

Freddy paused to see if Ralph or I would rise to that lure. Rather than disappoint such an enthusiast, I asked, "How about the Regular division?"

"Look!" He jabbed an emphatic finger at one set of figures. "In that engagement, the Regular division was operating independently and it had more psychiatric cases than the other two divisions put together."

Ralph and I digested that for a while before I asked, "Do those figures refer only to the number of actual psychoneurotics, or do they also include the dead-beats and gold-bricks?"

"Those figures reflect the true psychiatric cases," Freddy replied, but hastened to add, "although, along with every one hundred psychoneurotics who start back through the evacuation pipeline there will be about fifty of the other kind who are eventually screened out and eliminated."

"Aha!" said Ralph. "I think I get what you are talking about. Those men all look alike to the commanders, so the natural inference is that there is no difference between the psychoneurotic and the gold-brick. Is that about right?"

"Right on the nose!" Freddy applauded. "But it goes even farther than that. For instance, the fact that a man might wet himself or defecate as the result of fear has long been the basis for many a coarse joke. Consequently, any poor devil who becomes afflicted that way is made fun of and looked down upon as a coward. Those are the most commonly known reactions to stress. When it comes to hysterical conversion, severe anxiety and depressive states, the average person understands very little and, for lack of anything better, attributes them also to cowardice."

"But the fact remains that they all are the results of fear!" I stated.

"True," Freddy admitted, freely, "but those results are very concrete and real. If a soldier contracts a severe case of dysentery from drinking impure water, his commander feels sorry for him and is glad to see the man sent to a hospital. But if the soldier becomes afflicted with an equivalent ailment from stress and strain, that same commander becomes incensed and wants the soldier court-martialed."

"Then the only remedy is to eliminate fear!" I remarked, dryly.

Freddy shook his head and pointed to some of the ribbons on my chest. "If you got those where I think you did, you know very well there is no way to eliminate fear. It can be controlled but only by pride and determination! It certainly is not helped by ridicule or punishment!"

"How about fear of punishment?" I asked. "Can't that be employed successfully to combat other fears?"

"Such has certainly been the Army idea," Freddy admitted. "But by my way of figuring, it has not been very successful. I don't believe a man who reacts abnormally to one fear is going to be a better soldier if he has to choose the lesser of two very great fears."

"On the other hand," I argued, "there is the thought that a man can only react to one fear at a time and that would be the greater one."

Freddy could not agree. "You are talking like all the others. You are confusing the dead-beats with the psychoneurotics. If a malingerer knew he would surely be shot for deserting his duty he might prefer to stay and take his chances with the enemy. But a psychoneurotic's disorders have already occurred. They cannot be cured by a greater fear; they would only be aggravated!"

I turned to Ralph in hope of some further ideas but he only shrugged resignedly, "All I can think of is to ask the Doc just how we go about restoring or instilling pride and determination in these bozos who never had enough to begin with."

Freddy passed a tired hand across his brow and replied, a

little sadly, "God knows, perhaps, but that knowledge has not been vouchsafed me!"

Ralph was still grumbling over that last remark of Freddy's as we descended from our car and walked across the open terrace fronting the hotel in which we were billeted. The sun shone warmly and all the little metal tables on the terrace were well patronized by British, French and American officers. Suddenly, for no reason that I could see, Ralph halted and came to a distinct point. "What's wrong?" I asked, a trifle sharply. "Can't you wait until we get upstairs for a drink?"

"Look!" he said, gripping my arm. "We've just about consulted everybody we know in the Army and our last guy passes the buck to God. Well, why don't we ask him what the answer is?"

Following the direction indicated by Ralph's extended arm, I saw a lone officer seated at one of the little tables. He was a tall, slender man with merry blue eyes, offset by a square, determined chin. Over his left breast was the ribbon of the Purple Heart while the collar of his blouse displayed the cross. An Army chaplain!

"Padre," I said, stepping over and placing my hand on the back of the chair nearest to him, "would we be intruding?"

The blue eyes ran over me quickly and then Ralph. "Not at all," he waved for us to be seated. "A little wine?" he suggested. "In this country it is good for the stomach."

We sat down and called a waiter to take our order.

"Padre," I started out, "we have a problem I think you could help us with."

He waited inquiringly. "An appreciable number of our people have run away from the Army, or the gang-plank and the front lines. They don't want to be soldiers, they want to avoid risks and they're afraid to fight. Some get sick and are called psychoneurotics but, sick or well, the results are the same. Our doctors and commanders do not see eye to eye on the subject. The last doctor we talked with suggested that only God knew the answer, which may be so, but we thought that you might tell us if God ever referred to such matters."

A slow smile warmed the friendliness of the Padre's face. His eyes went skyward for a moment and then back to mine. "That, indeed, is a coincidence," he took a sip of wine.

"A coincidence?" Ralph and I edged forward eagerly.

The Padre nodded. "I've been thinking about that subject for some time, trying to arrange its meaning in my mind. Have you ever heard of Gideon's Three Hundred Men?"

Ralph and I exchanged sheepish glances, but the Padre smiled forgivingly, before resuming.

"Well, the Midianites were causing Gideon and his people a great deal of trouble and grief, so Gideon's people were all assembled. It looked very much as though there would be a great battle." The Padre sipped his wine with relish. "Now, the Lord was on Gideon's side so he told Gideon to proclaim in the ears of the people, 'Whosoever is fearful and afraid, let him return and depart early from Mt. Gilead.' So two and twenty thousand of them went home, leaving only ten thousand!"

"Jeepers," said Ralph, "were two-thirds of them too scared to fight?"

"Not only that," said the Padre, impressively, "but the Lord said to Gideon, 'The people are yet too many. Bring them down to the water and I will try them'."

"You mean he was going to find out if they'd get gang-plank fever?" Ralph demanded, incredulously.

The Padre held up an admonishing hand. "There were no

ships," he said, gently. "But when Gideon brought the people to the water the Lord said, 'Divide your forces. All that lappeth with his tongue, put him to one side and all of them who bend down on their knees to drink water will be put on the other side.' And only three hundred men lapped the water, and the Lord told Gideon that that would be the number he would take to defeat the Midianites."

Ralph looked at me in his disappointment and then down at his wine. Evidently he thought the story too far-fetched or else inapplicable to our own problem. So, as a matter of fact, did I.

"Gideon, of course, defeated the Midianites," Ralph offered in politeness.

The Padre undoubtedly sensed our dissatisfaction with his simile, but if so, he remained unperturbed. "Yes," he announced. "The Midianites were defeated and two of their Princes were captured. It was God's will!"

Ralph and I thanked him for his time, paid for our wine and excused ourselves.

"Huh!" said Ralph, as we walked from the table. "Three hundred men out of thirty thousand. That may have been all right in those times, but it wouldn't work out now."

"No," I agreed, "that would only be one man out of every hundred. The other guys would have too many of their own people against us. That is," I added, with no meaning of impiety, "unless we had God's help, also."

"Wait a minute," Ralph halted, suddenly, "when Gideon started out he had all of his people, didn't he?"

"That's right."

"Well, we didn't start out with *all* our people, only the ones who were drafted. And even then, nearly twenty-five per cent of them were rejected for psychoneurosis alone, remember?"

"Yeah!"

"Then about another ten or fifteen per cent were eliminated during the training period, weren't they?"

"As far as I remember, those were the figures."

"And after that still more jumped the gang-plank," Ralph massaged his forehead with the back of one hand. "Now we find out that approximately twenty to thirty per cent of all casualties are psychiatric cases. If you add all those together, the Padre's story doesn't sound so damn far off the beam, after all!"

"No," I admitted, thoughtfully, "and I can see now that there was a darn good moral behind it, too. Maybe we better go back and tell him . . ."

Before I could finish, an excited young staff officer came hurrying across the terrace. "Have you heard the news?" he cried.

"What news?" we asked.

"The *Afrika Korps* has surrendered! The campaign is over! We've won!"

Amid the joyful babbling which broke loose following that announcement, Ralph and I regarded each other with a trifle of awe in our eyes. We turned simultaneously to the table where we had left the Padre.

But his chair was empty. The Padre had gone.

Chapter 10

Female Of The Species

~~~~~~

The allies had won a great victory: hitler's *Afrika Korps* had surrendered in Tunisia and there was to be a breathing spell before the next campaign could be launched. So Ralph Bing and I decided we might just as well return to the United States by surface vessel.

No need to polish aluminum bucket seats with the back of our pants for two or more nights and days when ships were returning home practically empty. Why not cross the ocean in comfort, with bunks to sleep in and a deck to stroll upon? Discounting submarines, there would be nothing to worry about—or so we thought.

Certainly, there was no difficulty in securing passage. Ample space was available and, although still suggestive of "double bunking" and other conditions common to eastward voyages, our accommodations were comparable to what might be expected by a summer tourist putting up at a winter-resort hotel. And, when the ship's captain invited us to join his cabin mess, it looked very much as though we had hit the jackpot.

During our first meal at sea, however, we began to have some doubts and premonitions because the plates had hardly been cleared away before the Skipper said, "Do you know, I'm a little worried about those soldiers quartered down on C Deck."

"Sure enough?" I encouraged politely. "Who and what are they?"

"Well," the Skipper took his time in lighting a cigar, "that's just the point. I'm not too sure what they are. The passenger list shows them as 'NP Patients'."

159

Ralph and I had become accustomed to surprises. Without exchanging glances, we knew that each of us was wondering if the Skipper had somehow learned or been informed of the mission in which we were engaged.

"Are any of them psychotics, or in the locked ward category?" I inquired.

"Not that I know of," the Skipper hastily produced and scanned a typewritten list of names. "It says here they are psychoneurotics. But they didn't have any attendants with 'em, and there're no instructions to lock them up or anything like that."

"Then what's bothering you?" I asked a trifle puzzled. "They're not likely to cause any trouble."

The Skipper puffed violently on his cigar before saying, "But supposing some of them jump overboard?"

Taken by surprise, I nearly choked over the last swallow of the after-dinner coffee I had been nursing. There was, of course, the possibility of some severe depressive throwing away his own life, but a wholesale jumping over the rail, as evidently envisioned and feared by the Skipper, was so foreign to the general pattern of psychoneurotic behavior in North Africa, that I might well have been pardoned for saying, somewhat facetiously, "So what? If those guys would rather not have to face the ordeal of explaining to homefolks the cause for their being brought back, what do you care?"

The Skipper was properly shocked. "After all," he said, a little severely, "the Captain of a ship is responsible for the safety of his passengers."

"Are those psychos the only passengers you're perturbed about?" Ralph interposed smoothly.

The Skipper, thrown slightly out of gear by Ralph's practiced teamwork, almost shouted in return, "No, Goddammit! There are only about three hundred of them and in contrast I have four hundred seriously wounded—amputees! But, in addition, I've got almost as many GI prisoners, a bunch of casuals like yourselves, some WACs and a few USO people."

Ralph put down his cigar, which he didn't like very much anyhow, and asked, "What is the status of the WACs?"

The Skipper shrugged. "I don't know. They're not classified as NPs exactly, but all of them are being sent home for cause. And I have to keep them segregated, with a guard at each end of their companionway. A nice shipload I've got! Lunatics, prisoners, women with something wrong with them and —" he paused or caught himself so Ralph finished for him, "and inspectors general."

"Well," the Skipper had a salty smile, "we don't have 'em in the Navy."

"Never mind," said Ralph, "I bet you'll be glad we're aboard before we get to New York."

"I certainly will," Skipper retorted, "if you can play cribbage." And darned if the old walrus didn't take three dollars away from us that very night.

As we were getting ready to turn in for some sleep I said, "Listen, Ralph, it's supposed to be bad luck at sea to whistle for a wind or anything like that. You'd better not talk any more about the Skipper needing an inspector general or the first thing you know we'll run into some kind of trouble."

"Trouble?" Ralph yawned. "Why we're the same as being on a leave of absence. What kind of trouble are you talking about?"

I didn't know right then, but the next morning we found out. At breakfast word came that one of the WAC officers

aboard had demanded an interview with the inspector general
—officially and alone. That presented a minor problem. No
woman could enter a man's stateroom and men could not tres-
pass in that part of the ship where women were quartered. The
problem was solved by arranging a meeting in the office of the
troop-transport commander. And Ralph, the bum, pointed out
that, as the senior, it was my duty to conduct the hearing.

I retaliated by not telling him what transpired, although he
later tried many wiles and cajolery to find out.

Actually, upon meeting the WAC officer it was rather difficult to believe that her complaints if any were of a serious nature. Although in her late thirties she certainly filled out her
uniform in a way the original designers would indubitably have
approved. But the smoldering fire in her eyes was in no way
related to topography.

"I want to know," she started out belligerently, "why I was
relieved from my command."

Not even knowing what her command had been I was somewhat at a loss.

"Didn't anyone tell you why you were relieved?" I ventured.

"No! I was suddenly sent to a hospital," her full lips almost
spat the last word, "and a psychiatrist asked me questions for
which if my husband had been present he would have been
shot!"

Jeepers, I thought frantically, where's my inspector's guide
on this? My voice tasted like skimmed milk diluted with water
when I asked, "What kind of questions?"

Her slightly faded auburn hair seemed to pulse like a neon
light. "He asked questions about my sex life! Not just general-
ities, but particulars! If I hadn't wanted to keep my commission
and my command I would have scratched the eyes right out of

his face. But I lost my command anyhow and now I want to know why."

Oh boy! Oh, Jimmy-the-Hard and some of those other guys who thought they knew all the answers! Just to have had one of them there to pass that one on to. But I didn't even have Ralph, so I asked a trifle timidly, "Meaning no offense, but just where did the sex angle enter into it?"

"That is what I would like to know," she planted both feet squarely on the deck, with knees slightly apart and displaying a little more than strictly GI. But her posture was in no way seductive because she was fighting mad. "They seemed to think I was sadistic, or frustrated, or something, when I made my personnel toe the line and punished them when they didn't. Just because I required one enlisted woman to walk the area with a pack on her back for having stayed out of barracks after bed check, the psychiatrist asked me if I wasn't jealous of the man she had been out with."

"Jealous of the man?" I raised an eyebrow. "You mean of the woman."

"No, I don't," she snapped right back, "I mean of the man. The psychiatrist was trying to make me admit to abnormal tendencies. Of course, he did not succeed as the records will show. Nevertheless, I was relieved of my command and am being sent home."

Trying to ease the situation I produced some cigarettes, but she would have none of them. I asked, "Do you know who requested your relief?"

"No! But I have my suspicions," she said darkly. "My second in command and some of her friends have been working against me ever since we first left the United States. Of course," she indulged in a ladylike sneer, "they also were detailed to work at headquarters. That is why I think the whole thing should be investigated."

I assured the lady that the matter would be looked into. As soon as she had departed, I sent for her records along with the Army medical officer aboard ship.

"What's the score on this case?" I asked showing him the file.

After some study and consideration he shrugged. "Oh, nothing unusual here. Just a little mental instability brought about by the menopause. 'Shouldn't command troops under such conditions'," he half mumbled, half read from the record, " 'sent home for other assignment!' "

"Mental instability," I repeated sharply. "Does that indicate the presence of a psychosis or neurosis?"

The doctor snapped erect as though he'd suddenly remembered leaving a light on during blackout hours.

"There is no such diagnosis here," he tapped the record with a forefinger.

"Whether it's in the record or not," I persisted, "would a person showing some mental instability because of the menopause be considered in the same category as a psychoneurotic or psychotic?"

The doc scrubbed his chin violently with the palm of one hand.

"It all depends," he hedged. "During the menopause the personality traits of a woman are greatly exaggerated. Also there usually is a decided trend toward the paranoia."

"Paranoia? You mean insanity?"

"No, no! Not necessarily, at all. Just a delusion of persecution, combined with hallucinations of one's own great importance."

"Good grief," I was surprised into a laugh. "If that's the case, it couldn't be entirely confined to women. But with regard to the exaggeration of women's traits during the menopause, do you mean whatever they might be normally is magnified during that particular period of life?"

"Not exactly. Say rather, that whatever traits they demonstrate during the menopause is an exaggeration of what has been part of their personality all the time, even if in a subconscious or dormant state."

"Oh, my God," I groaned dropping my head in my hands. "Let me see if I get this straight. If, for example, a woman had any latent homosexual tendencies she would not necessarily be forced into committing overt acts during the menopause, but if she turned out to be sadistic and cruel during that period it would be because she had harbored such traits all the time. It would only be that she lost control during a certain time of life. Is that what you are telling me?"

"Such at least is my firm belief," agreed the doc.

"Look," I said, "are men afflicted with similar periods in life? Is that where the saying comes from, that so-and-so is 'acting like an old woman'?"

It was the doc's turn to laugh. "You may have something there, sir, but I am not prepared to discuss it."

"Well," I sighed, "this certainly has been illuminating but right now I think I need some air." So getting to my feet I went outside in search of Ralph. I found him just coming from the ship's stores with several cartons of cigarettes in his arms.

"What's the idea?" I exclaimed somewhat annoyed. "Don't you know the ration is only one pack a day?"

"Nuts!" he retorted with eyes sparkling. "Come on and meet some friends I just found."

None too willingly I followed him along the starboard deck and down a ladder. We landed in a large, white painted compartment filled with double-decked bunks. An improvised hospital ward!

"Hey!" Ralph announced loudly while shoving some of the cartons at me. "Free smokes!"

As I somewhat clumsily opened the packages to help distribute Ralph's gift I gazed about at the open, eager faces peering over the edge of each bunk. What made me awkward and brought a lump to my throat was the sudden realization that there was not a single one of them but was minus a leg or an arm. And all too frequently I had to pause long enough to put a cigarette in a boy's mouth and strike a match because the lad had no means of doing it himself. Despite that and although I searched each face closely I saw none of the dull, vacant-eyed fatalism so often observed in so many of the NP wards Ralph and I had visited. Yet those had been alive and whole while these others were maimed, terribly maimed for life.

"How did it happen?" I asked casually of one boy whose cigarette needed to be lit.

"A mine," he smiled back. "I heaved a rock out of my foxhole and it hit a mine that exploded."

Before I could frame a reply the boy's upper bunkmate gibed in fun, "Gowan! Why don't you tell him the truth? You tried to liberate a bottle of wine and it turned out to be a booby trap!"

The lad I had first spoken to just grinned and puffed contentedly on his cigarette, but another patient across the way came immediately to his defense.

"Yeah! And how about him?" indicating the facetious one. "Ask him about the time he's driving a jeep an' the road ain't good enough for him even though he's bringin' our coffee ration for the day. He has to take a shortcut just because the Krauts are droppin' a few measly shells on the road. He thinks he knows where the minefields are. Well, first we see him comin' hell for leather across an open space, and the next we see he's sailing through the air holdin' on to the steerin' wheel but without what it takes to put on the brakes. An' there goes our coffee ration."

And so it went, no complaints, no grumbling, no self pity.

"Look," I finally accosted the ward surgeon, "are there any psychoneurotics among this bunch of GIs?"

He stared his surprise. "Good God, no! Of course not. They're all perfectly normal."

I winced a trifle at the use of that word under the circumstances. "But if any group of men had reason to be morose or neurotic, it would be these."

The surgeon shook his head emphatically. "There's not a more cheerful lot of people on the ship," he insisted and I could see no evidence to disprove his statement.

"Then can you tell me why they are in such good spirits?"

He looked thoughtfully into a stethoscope as though seeking the answer there. "Honestly, I don't know. Of course, we do everything for them we possibly can but it's not just that. I really think it is because for them the war is finished. They know they have difficult periods of adjustment ahead, but that is in the distant future. Right now each of them knows he demonstrated individual bravery and courage. So they are not going to give in now. Instead they are at peace with themselves and are enjoying a mental rest free from fear and stress."

"More power to them," I said meaningly. "They certainly have earned the right to act in any way they choose. And rewards for anything less than what they have given should certainly be judged accordingly."

I walked back between the tiers of bunks and climbed the ladder on my way to the stateroom assigned to Ralph and me. At first I thought the sight of so many battle-torn youngsters, together with the smells of a hospital ward, had made me feel unwell but as I proceeded along the deck I realized the sea was rising rapidly.

Before nightfall we were in the midst of a terrific storm and it was four days before I could do much more than lie in my bunk and hope for the best; the only consolation being that Ralph was similarly engaged and suffered with each roll of the ship as much as I.

When the storm had passed we both struggled up on deck for fresh air and information as to how the rest of the passengers had fared. One of the first persons we ran into was the ship's doctor.

"How's everybody doing, Doc?" I asked.

"Not so good," he replied. "A couple of WACs were thrown out of their bunks and got hurt!"

"Badly?"

"Well, one of them broke a rib and the other I'm afraid has a concussion."

"That's bad enough," Ralph acknowledged and then seeing the Doc was reluctant to leave us he asked, "Anything else?"

"Yes!" Doc evidently was eager to unburden himself. "I'm having trouble with some other WACs, too."

"What kind of trouble?" I asked.

"It's probably my fault," Doc hastened to say, "but during the storm right after those girls had fallen out of their upper bunks I advised all of them to double up in the lower bunks."

"What of it?" Ralph asked. "They're all women, aren't they?"

"That's just it," Doc replied. "The WAC captain in charge says there were some not so womanly among them, and had three put into solitary confinement!"

"Is it the same WAC officer who complained to me?" I demanded.

"No," the Doc answered, "this is still another one."

"Hey!" Ralph turned to me accusingly. "What goes on here? You haven't told me yet what you and that WAC talked about."

"No, I haven't. But you are going to be in on this one from the ground floor up. What is this other WAC officer being sent home for?" I asked Doc.

"She's pregnant," then, seeing the look on our faces, Doc hastened to add, "Oh, it's all right! She's married and has a husband but now she has to be discharged."

"Did the Skipper put an O.K. on those three women being thrown in the brig?" Ralph queried.

"Hey!" Doc objected. "They're not in the brig; just in single staterooms. More like 'medical restraint,' as it's called."

"Are the rooms locked and under guard?"

"Well, yes."

"Huh!" Ralph grunted. "Then it's the same thing as being in the brig, isn't it?"

"Maybe," Doc grinned, "but the other sounds better."

"And did the Skipper approve?" Ralph returned to his original question, "Or didn't you tell him?"

"Of course, I told him. But he's a busy man. He said it was up to the WAC Captain and if the Army insisted on putting its women in solitary it was all right with him."

"Well, it's not all right with us," I stated emphatically. "Let's have that Captain down in your office and have a talk with her."

The Captain was tall, good looking, with snapping black eyes and determination written all over her. I couldn't help but wonder what she was going to say to her husband about being brought home to be discharged but that, of course, was none of my business. So I concentrated on what we were there to discuss.

"What evidence have you," I went right to the point, "against those three women you had put in solitary?"

"I've known them for a long time," her little white teeth clicked out the words. "They all three are members of a group that had somehow gotten together overseas. We tried to break it up and that is why some of them are being sent home."

"That's as it may be, Captain," I said sharply. "But what I want to know is did they misbehave in any way aboard this ship?"

The Captain's eyes flashed from me to the Doc but she did not answer. Her mouth set in a prim little straight line.

"Listen," I said somewhat angrily, "this is no time for delicate feelings. Three enlisted women to all intent and purposes have been placed in confinement. They must either be released immediately or else have charges preferred against them. Are you prepared to do that?"

The Captain's assurance began to melt. "Two of them have been sleeping in the same bunk ever since the ship sailed," she declared defensively. "One of them was a corporal and the third, a Sergeant Jones, became jealous, so she and the corporal had a fight. I thought it best that all three be separated and kept apart."

"Is that the reason for their being put under 'medical restraint'?" I turned on Doc.

"Of course not!" he stated flatly. "This Captain," he nodded in the WAC's direction, "charged them with being homosexuals. I understood they would be placed before a Board of Officers to be discharged from the service."

"But they were going home to be discharged anyhow, weren't they?" Ralph asked.

"Yes," the Captain spoke up, "but I should think it would be in the best interest of the government to discharge them according to their deserts, not to get out for dependency or any other honorable reasons!"

"I understand you also are returning to be discharged," I said pointedly. "Are you willing to delay your separation in order to testify at the hearing of these women?"

"I do not believe I would be in a condition to appear before a court," the Captain retreated behind her feminine dignity, "and besides, I feel sure that plenty of other witnesses could be found without me."

"Then you don't wish to be the one to prefer formal charges against them?" I persisted.

The Captain shook her head.

"That being the case," I said to Doc, "we will excuse the Captain but I would like to hear what those other women have to say for themselves."

The first to appear was Private Wells, the one the sergeant and corporal purportedly had fought over. She was about twenty-five or six, and best described as "fluffy."

"Why are you being returned to the United States for discharge?" I asked bypassing the usual formalities of an inquiry.

"When I enlisted, sir," she replied calmly, "I left my five-year-old daughter with my mother. Recently my mother died so I requested that I be discharged so as to take care of my child."

"Where is your husband?" asked Ralph.

"I don't know, sir," she answered, "we have been separated for some time."

That seemed to be that so I asked bluntly, "Have you engaged in any illicit relations with the WAC corporal you have been sharing your bunk with?"

Her somewhat thick lips twisted contemptuously. "If the corporal were a man my answer might be different but as it is I can truthfully say no! Ever since I joined the WACs I've heard about homosexuals, but so far as I'm concerned it's all been talk."

I looked inquiringly at Ralph but he signalled positively that he had nothing further to ask. We dismissed Private Wells and sent for the corporal.

Under other conditions she would have impressed me as being strikingly good looking. She had a full mouth, high cheek bones, with large, slanting blue eyes. But her hair was cut in mannish style and she wore slacks instead of a skirt. Upon being seated she regarded us with a cool and none too friendly gaze.

"What is the reason for your being sent home?" I started out.

"The other officers were jealous of our captain," the tone of her voice was strictly feminine, without a trace of mannish mannerism. "We did more and better work than any of the other groups over there. We were all friends and kept to ourselves, so to get even, I think, a lot of the other women began saying we were 'queer' and things like that. Finally they were going to break up our group and transfer us all to other outfits. About that time my two brothers were killed in the Pacific and I thought I was needed more at home than where I was being sent so I asked for a discharge."

"Your brothers were in the service?" Ralph asked interestedly.

"Yes, sir! One in the Marines and one in the Army. They were killed within a month of each other."

Ralph's jaw set at its most pugnacious angle and his eyes told me plainly that he would have nothing more to do with interrogating a woman whose two brothers had died for their country. Nevertheless I thought one more question necessary for the record so I asked it. "If you were placed under oath would you be willing to swear that the allegations regarding your being 'queer' were without foundation?"

The corporal's chin seemed almost as firm as Ralph's when she answered, "I certainly would. There is nothing queer about me except that I like my friends and stand by them."

"Is that why you and Sergeant Jones had a fight?"

"Yes! She was picking on Private Marjorie Wells," the corporal's slant eyes snapped. "Marjorie was sick but the sergeant told her if she didn't get out of bed and help sweep up the deck she'd pull her out. I told the sergeant to leave Marjorie alone, so Jones slapped me and I slapped her back. That was all there was to it."

I looked at Ralph but he still refused to ask any questions so I let the corporal go. Next we had Sergeant Jones and when she entered the office I had a shock. She also effected a mannish haircut and she was much older than the other two. But what gave me a jolt was the manner in which she walked, sat and talked. If she hadn't worn a skirt and filled her blouse in certain places, I'd have sworn she was any one of a dozen Regular Army sergeants who had served under me at one time or another over a period of twenty years or more. And like them she looked hard and tough.

"Sergeant," I said, wasting no preliminaries on her, "do you know why you have been placed in a room by yourself?"

"I know what they say," she replied promptly, "because they've said it."

"Do you deny it?"

"I do, sir! Now and to my dying day!"

It was difficult to proceed from there. That she was mannish in appearance and demeanor was undeniable, but I remembered in past interviews with male homosexuals that they had freely admitted their weakness, particularly if they thought it would get them out of the Army. What then, could be done in the case of a flat denial. Again I sought Ralph's counsel but he refused to be involved.

When the sergeant had gone Ralph, Doc and I regarded each other inquiringly.

"Well?" I prompted. "What's the verdict?"

"Nuts!" Ralph exploded in one of his pet expressions. "There's nothing to it."

I waited inquiringly for Doc.

"I'm not so sure," he finally said.

"You're a lousy cynic," Ralph accused.

"Sure," Doc grinned, "but that is because I am also a doctor and have had a great many women patients. Most women dress and act in a way to attract men. Did *they* attract you?"

"Don't get personal," Ralph retorted.

"I'm not trying to be," Doc replied seriously. "But if a woman is not interested in men and trying to attract them she's either an old maid at heart or something else, and I don't think the corporal and the sergeant are of the old maid type!"

"To hell with all that!" I entered the argument. "It's of academic interest only so far as I'm concerned. The point is, are there any reasons or for that matter sufficient evidence to justify having those women locked up? If not, then we've got to do something about it."

Doc shrugged. "I suppose if we had a psychiatrist aboard we could get a diagnosis on them. That's what I intended to do as soon as we reached port, turn them over to a psychiatrist."

"And until then you'd take part in locking up three women, one whose mother has just died and another who'd lost two brothers in the war?" Ralph accused. "All on the word of a pregnant WAC?"

Doc got up and walked around the office uneasily. "Goddammit, I certainly thought it was the correct procedure until you started talking, but now I'm not so sure. Maybe we'd better go see the Skipper."

That salty old barnacle was not at all pleased with our bringing the problem to him. "What the hell do I have a ship's doctor for?" He glared at the unhappy Doc and then turned on me. "I told you we had a lot of nuts and psychoneurotics aboard this ship and you were the very one who advised me not to pay any attention to them!"

"That's right," I agreed. "And I'm still telling you the same thing. Turn them all loose and forget about 'em."

For awhile he puffed vigorously on a smelly, short-stemmed pipe. His eyes popped out crab-like, first at Doc, then at Ralph and lastly at me. "If I do," he finally said, "and anything goes wrong, damned if I don't put all three of you in the brig."

He certainly meant it although his very earnestness made me laugh. "Skipper," I said, "the more attention you pay those people the more trouble you are going to have with them. But if you just treat them like anybody else no one will ever know there is anything the matter with them. They are not going to do anything out of the way, now they are so close to home. And if one of them does you can put me on bread and water."

The Skipper's pipe gurgled like a hubble-bubble while he thought the matter over. "All right," he finally agreed, "I'll give 'em the run of the ship," and then he added ominously, "but if any of 'em blow their tops before we reach New York, you three are due for a diet of H_2O."

He wasn't kidding either but as a matter of fact we continued to eat at the cabin mess all the way in.

CHAPTER 11
THAT PIECE OF PAPER

~~~~~~

WHEN RALPH BING AND I SET FOOT ON U. S. SOIL AGAIN after our tour overseas, there seemed to be but one phase remaining to button up our study on Army psychoneurotics; namely, to pay a visit to some of the Convalescent Hospitals where psychos are sent for rehabilitation and return to duty or for discharge.

So after submitting an interim report on our activities and findings to date, we journeyed to a large hospital in Florida not far from where we had first started our inquiry.

Upon arrival at the headquarters of that installation and during our initial conference with the commanding officer and his chief psychiatrist we were quickly enlightened regarding the actual functions of the hospital.

" 'Convalescent' is a misnomer for this place," the psychiatrist, a Captain Copton declared. "What we actually are is a medical separation center."

"What sort of medical cases do you handle or process?" I inquired.

Copton laughed a little bitterly I thought. "All kinds. General, Regional and sometimes even Station Hospitals have to clear their beds for new patients so they send everything they can to us."

"Including psychoneurotics?" asked Ralph.

"Including up to from thirty to forty percent psychoneurotics," Copton replied. "We have organized all our patients into three battalions. Those in the psychiatric department are in the 3d Battalion and it always has a greater strength than either of the other two."

"Who commands the companies in that battalion?" I asked.

"Those psychiatrists on duty with the hospital," the CO answered. "In that way they have direct and constant contact with their patients at all times."

"Now as I understand it," I said practically thinking out loud, "the other hospitals send these cases to you purportedly for convalescence, but actually for disposition. You either return them for duty or effect their discharge."

Both Copton and his CO indicated that as far as I had gone my thinking was correct.

"Then," I continued, "the sixty-four dollar question is how many do you return to duty and how many do you discharge?"

The psychiatrist and his chief exchanged pleased glances exactly like a school superintendent and his head teacher applauding the performance of a star pupil. It was Copton who elected to answer.

"You are no doubt familiar with the methods by which we at a Convalescent Hospital dispose of our patients," he began as a warm-up to the subject.

"I believe we are," I admitted, "but suppose you tell us just to be sure."

He accepted the invitation with alacrity. "One possible method of separation is to prove that an individual possesses traits and character sufficiently undesirable to warrant discharge in which case the discharge is neither honorable nor dishonorable. I presume you both have had experience in attempting to prove such an allegation before a Board of Officers?"

Ralph and I indicated that we had.

"Then you know it is the accuser and not the accused who ends up being under trial. So that pretty well eliminates method number one. Next there is the possibility of establishing the fact that an individual is inapt or unadaptable to the service. Perhaps you have had experience in that field also?"

Again Ralph and I nodded that we had.

"Then," Copton went on, "I need not tell you of the futility of such a task in the face of a service record wherein a series of previous commanders have given ratings of 'satisfactory' or better to the person under consideration in order that he might be eligible for transfer elsewhere when the opportunity arose."

Ralph's grin and mine assured him that he need not go into details.

"In all fairness," Copton went on, "I honestly believe the reason those Boards lean over backward is because they believe that by curtailing the number of men separated for undesirable traits and character and also for inaptitude they are saving manpower and forcing more soldiers to continue in the service. Actually, however, they leave us but one of two alternatives. We either return our patients to duty or else give them a CDD or disability discharge."

"Have you," I asked hopefully, "any figures on the actual number of psychoneurotics returned to duty and separated under each category?"

"I certainly have," Copton replied producing a previously prepared paper from one of his pockets. "Believe it or not six percent were separated for traits of character and inaptitude, sixteen percent were returned to duty and seventy-eight percent have been given a disability discharge."

Ralph shook his head despondently and said to me, "What a hell of a way to run an Army!"

"Yeah," I agreed. "But I can't see why so few are returned to duty. Are they all that sick?"

"They're all sick of the Army," Copton replied frankly. "We

are able to effect a certain degree of recovery but return them to duty and they will immediately have a recurrence of their disorders."

"How about the sixteen percent that are returned to duty?" Ralph asked quickly. "Don't they get along all right?"

"On the contrary," Copton shook his head, "there is every evidence and considerable reason to believe that they practically all get back into medical channels again in a very short period of time and start going through the same process all over again."

"In that event," I sighed, "it must be your opinion that other than the five or six percent of psychoneurotics you manage to discharge for reasons other than honorable, approximately ninety-five percent of them obtain a disability discharge in the long-run and probably a pension and other benefits and compensation later on."

"As a Reserve officer and future taxpayer I hope I'm wrong," Copton replied sadly. "But I'm afraid that what you said is correct."

I looked inquiringly at the CO who shook his head in negation. "Captain Copton and I have discussed this problem many times but there does not appear to be any solution. We are convinced that military service is repugnant to such a large majority of our people that their sympathy and protection are immediately extended to anyone unable to endure its demands and sacrifices regardless of the reason for a failure to do so."

"It seems to me then," Ralph began to summarize, "that if a psychoneurotic is called upon to serve his country he or she sooner or later breaks down under stress and becomes a burden instead of a help to the people."

"I won't go so far as to agree that every psychoneurotic will break down," Copton stated. "Some may never reach their breaking point or encounter the kind of stress that would make them break."

"Meaning that each person has a different thing or a different amount of the same thing that might break him down?" I interposed.

"But certainly," Copton looked surprised that I would ask the question.

"Maybe so," Ralph said, "but for us it just boils down to this: There are only two over-all groups, those who begin to show psychoneurotic symptoms the minute they get in the Army and those whose symptoms hold off until they get into combat."

"Oh, no!" Copton replied. "There are plenty who don't break down because they never get in combat or don't stay in it long enough to reach the breaking point."

"I suppose we all could be subjected to sufficient stress or strain to make us break if we were kept at it long enough," I said.

"Certainly!" both doctors agreed.

"But supposing the time comes when there aren't enough non-psychoneurotics in our country to win a war?" Ralph demanded. "What then?"

"Let's hope that time never comes," the CO replied fervently.

"At any rate," I said getting ready to terminate the conference, "it hasn't arrived yet and if anybody doesn't believe it all he has to do is go out and count our prisoners. In the meantime we had better continue on our way to see how conditions are in some of the other convalescent hospitals."

Copton smiled confidently. "I don't think you will find anything much different than right here," he said.

In that he was entirely correct. The airplane assigned to our mission took Ralph and me from one installation to another pretty well boxing the compass in our course. At each place visited the story was pretty much the same, although not all the psychiatrists we met were quite as open and frankspoken as Copton. But the records were very much the same, never less than seventy-five percent of all psychoneurotic cases being discharged for physical disability.

At one hospital an amusing incident occurred. Upon our arrival we found close to a hundred patients in the NP ward, all of whom had progressed through medical channels to a point where they were reasonably assured and consequently confident of receiving disability discharges. We could not help but notice that although they were all in hospital garb they were engaged in such occupations as pitching horseshoes, playing softball and otherwise deporting themselves as gentlemen of leisure.

"A fairly contented lot," I observed dryly to the commanding officer who accompanied us.

"Well," he replied, a little on the defensive side, "they're all up for disability discharges."

During a conference held later with him and his staff Ralph and I indicated that in our opinion disability discharges were being handed out a bit too freely.

We took off next morning but a cold front closed in and our pilot was ordered to return to the base we had just departed from. The commanding officer of the hospital, as a matter of courtesy, again was on hand to receive us. From his demeanor I gathered that our unexpected return had embarrassed him.

"Please don't let us bother you," I tried to set him at ease. "Our inspection is over and we're just a couple of transients now."

But he didn't see it that way. "You remember those NP patients you looked at yesterday?"

"Sure," Ralph chirped up. "One of them had all the ear-marks of a champion horseshoe pitcher and some of the rest were pretty good ball players."

The commanding officer appealed to me for understanding. "That's just the point. Somehow what you said in our conference yesterday leaked out and got to the ears of those patients in the NP ward."

"Well," I shrugged, "what about it?"

The commanding officer almost blushed. "Today," he said, "when I made my rounds of inspection I discovered that every single one of them as of this morning was too sick to get out of bed. They all had to have their meals brought to them and each and every one of them are requiring medical attention."

"Meaning, I suppose, that our expressed disapproval regarding the ease with which a disability discharge was secured brought about a recurrence of their disorders?"

The commanding officer nodded. "On the face of it that appears to be the case."

"So what?" asked Ralph. "You can't hold us to blame for the reactions of those people."

"Of course not," replied the commanding officer. "But I was wondering if you would think I was lax in my duty if I didn't make some effort to prevent those discharges from going through."

"Not at all," I reassured him. "Actually you have a comparatively small number of psychoneurotics as compared to the over-all total. We appreciate your feelings in the matter but don't let it influence you into diverting from approved procedures. Our job is to establish facts and submit recommendations regarding policies as a whole, not in individual cases or instances."

The commanding officer's relief was both obvious and sincere. "I certainly hope you find the right answers," he said most fervently.

"You don't hope it any more than we do," Ralph quipped, "and right now our being weathered-in gives us a little more time to think it over."

But within a few hours the front which had delayed us moved past and once more we were on our way to Washington and fast approaching the time for reaching final conclusions on our study of psychoneurotics. We stopped at one more convalescent hospital and there met a psychiatrist as outspoken as Copton. His name was Moor.

"I'm not trying to kid myself or anybody else," he stated flatly. "As soon as a psychoneurotic is able to take care of himself I get him out of here."

"You mean return him to duty?" I asked.

"No," Moor retorted, "he gets a discharge."

"How many do you put up before a Board of Officers?" Ralph asked.

"I've given up trying that except in the most extreme cases having to do with undesirable traits of character," replied Moor. "All the Officers' Boards I've run into have the idea that a man must either be a general-duty soldier or else given a medical discharge. So I give them a discharge."

"Then you don't think they can ever be made into general-duty soldiers again?" I asked.

"If they could they never would have gotten as far as this through medical channels. By the time they get here the medical department has done all it could do for them."

"How about their going back into civil life?" demanded Ralph. "Are they able to take care of themselves all right?"

"Listen," Moor snapped, "nine-tenths of them are cured the minute they walk out the gate with a discharge in their hands."

"Jeepers!" I was startled into exclaiming. "Are you a psychiatrist?

"I am," he retorted, "and I've got papers to prove it. But perhaps you misunderstood my meaning. I was not implying that those cases were cured of being psychoneurotics."

"Then for Heaven's sake please explain what you did mean," I begged.

"Let me show you," he said and picking up a phone directed one of the wards to send over a certain one of their patients. "The individual you are going to see has about two and a half years' service and is now being discharged for physical disability."

When the man he had sent for walked in I noticed that he was a technical sergeant somewhere around twenty-five years of age. He was quiet, rather good looking, with a pleasant and respectful manner.

He admitted that he was feeling good and was more than pleased with the prospect of getting back to his wife and child.

"How about returning to duty?" I inquired experimentally.

A gloomy shadow perceptibly spread over his features and one eyelid began to twitch. "No, sir!" he stated emphatically. "I couldn't go back to that again."

"Hell!" Ralph burst out when the sergeant had gone. "He's as good looking a soldier as you'll find anywhere. I don't see anything the matter with him."

"You don't now," Moor replied, "but you would have four weeks ago; hands shaking so he couldn't lift a cup of coffee, one eye twitching all the time, and unable to get any sleep. That's what he was then and that's what he'd be again if he were sent back."

"Oh, oh," I said. "I think I begin to see what you were talking about when you said a discharge would cure most of them."

"It's rather obvious," said Moor, "their immediate disorders are caused by something which happened to them in the Army. Release them from the Army and in most cases the disorders disappear."

"But won't those disorders reappear at some future date and under other circumstances?" I asked.

"Quite probably. Particularly if they encounter situations where the stress is just as great."

"But they were psychoneurotic before they came into the Army, weren't they?"

"Certainly," Moor was quite emphatic.

"Then the Army could scarcely be charged justifiably with having aggravated their cases, could it?"

"That depends upon how you look at it," Moor replied. "Usually a psychoneurotic will manage to remove himself from a thing or place which brings about his pain or discomfort, providing of course that he knows what is causing it. That is where the science of psychiatry enters the picture; determining the cause and bringing it from the subconscious to the conscious. Well, it's not so difficult to discover the cause in the Army, but there isn't much can be done about it."

"Except to prescribe a discharge," said Ralph grimly. "Because the basic cause when you come right down to it is just the mere fact of being in the Army."

"You might sum it all up that way," said Moor, "but a psychiatrist cannot pick up a pad and write out a prescription for better leadership, more care in individual assignments, freedom from financial worries, more correct behavior on the part of some men's wives, or for any of the hundred other things which go towards bringing about the condition of these men."

"You didn't include fear of combat in your list," I said to see what he would reply.

"No, I didn't mention it but that doesn't mean that I deny its existence or even minimize its influence upon some of my patients. Just the same a large majority of the ones I've dealt with never saw combat and the greater proportion didn't even have assignments that would have required them to go near the front line."

"Then you do not associate cowardice with psychoneurosis?"

"That is not what I was saying," Moor shot back. "I simply pointed out that the greatest number of my patients never had any real reason to fear combat. Their breakdowns were due to other causes."

"Yes," I said, "but if they hadn't broken down before wouldn't they have cracked up under fire?"

For the first time Moor really smiled. "A scientist bases his findings upon facts, not conjectures. What I have told you are established facts."

"But scientists have theories like all the rest of us, don't they?" And when Moor nodded I added, "Now I have a theory which is shared by a good many other laymen, namely, that all psychoneurosis is based upon fear. Fear of combat, fear of personal harm, fear of ridicule, or anything else you want to add, but always fear. Everybody is afraid of something and if he is constantly subjected or exposed to the thing he is afraid of he will sooner or later crack up."

"Certainly each person has his own threshold or limit of endurance," Moor agreed.

"Then in that case we're all potential psychoneurotics, aren't we?" I asked.

"Possibly," Moor replied watching me alertly. "But not all people who crack up from fear are psychoneurotics if that is what you are getting at.

"How can you tell one from another?" Ralph asked quickly.

Moor grinned. "You bring them to me or to any other psychiatrist and we can tell the difference."

"How?" I asked skeptically.

"By their symptoms; by the way they react to fear."

Ralph and I thought that over for a moment before I tried another line of thought. "Doctor, tell me this: were all the men who have received disability discharges for psychoneurosis actually psychoneurotic, or have a lot of them been given that diagnosis to get them out of the Army simply because they weren't good soldiers and there was no other way to get rid of them?"

Moor regarded me intently before asking, "You want my professional or my personal opinion?"

"Whichever you care to give me."

"Then I will say that it is my personal opinion that there have been as many of one as of the other, and that has been plenty."

A swift interchange of glances between Ralph and me indicated that we were agreed Dr. Moor had told us all we could expect under the circumstances. Therefore, we bade him goodbye and started on the last leg of our journey to Washington.

"Well, Ralphie," I said as our plane gained altitude to clear the mountains of West Virginia, "have you come to any definite conclusions regarding these problems?"

"Not on all of them," he admitted, "but I certainly have very decided ideas on certain phases of this business of psychoneurosis."

"So have I," I sighed. "But I'm not so sure the Chief will like them, and I'm almost certain some of the neuropsychiatrists will resent them very much."

"All we can tell them is what we think and honestly believe," Ralph tried to reassure me. "They can't ask any more of us than that."

"I don't suppose they can," I said.

But we were wrong. There was one more task ahead as we found out upon reaching Washington. It appeared there was a major disagreement of ideas on some very high levels and I was immediately called upon to participate in discussing them at a hastily called staff conference. The disagreement was over the difference between psychoneurosis and "battle fatigue," and it turned out to be hot.

CHAPTER 12

THREE IN ONE

THE WAR DEPARTMENT CONFERENCE, ASSEMBLED FOR the purpose of discussing psychoneurotics in general, and those included in the category of "battle fatigue" particularly, was well attended. Colonel Still, of the Surgeon General's Office; Colonel Taylor for Air; Colonel Price, a Wac, representing G-1; and myself for the IGD. Also present were various henchmen armed with brief cases loaded with data.

The five eminent psychiatrists who had assisted General McIder, M.D., of our office, in conducting the technical side of the investigation in which Ralph Bing and I had operated on a very low-bombing level, had submitted their report and recommendations, which folio had been approved in toto. However, there still remained what the War Department referred to as "implementation." In other words, when the big shots announce a given policy or procedure, there have to be some pick-and-shovel guys around to put it into effect and see that it works.

Such were the boys—and girl—with whom I found myself in conference. They were not the heads of the various departments represented, but they packed plenty of authority and, as it soon became evident, carried some very definite instructions from their chiefs. It also was quickly apparent that not all of them saw eye to eye on certain subjects.

Colonel Price opened the conference with a statement. "The number of disability discharges for psychoneurosis has already reached well into six figures," she said, "and G-1 believes that a not inconsiderable number of those diagnoses have been incorrect!"

"Upon just what does G-1 base such a belief?" asked Colonel Still, more as a boxer tests an opponent's foot work rather than in the vein of argument.

"Why," the little Wac Colonel smiled brightly, "upon certain reports submitted by the Inspector General's Department." By a glance, she accomplished the same as a jerk of the thumb at me.

Right then I realized why I was present and also saw that I might well be called upon to defend some of the reports Ralph and I had submitted. However, on the subject mentioned, we had figures to substantiate Colonel Price's statement.

"There is no denying that the term 'psychoneurosis' has been loosely used, and even abused," Colonel Still admitted. "But do you believe it has been the fault of the Medical Corps?"

"No," I said emphatically, the "Medical Corps has been prostituted and forced into a position where they had to wash dirty linen for the Line!"

"Then something must be done about it," said Colonel Price firmly. "The question is, what?"

"That's easy," I said, "but first tell us, of all the disability discharges given for psychoneurosis, how many cases originated in combat and how many did not?"

Immediately, I noticed that Colonel Taylor and his group from Air Came to the alert, as Colonel Price prepared to answer my question.

"We do not have definite figures regarding the combat cases," she said, "but we do know that 800 out of every 1,000 psychoneurotics discharged never served outside the continental limits of the United States. Your department," indicating me, "has investigated many of those cases and my own corps has also. One of them is typical." She began to tell us about that case.

A young and very pretty girl from a good family had enlisted in the WAC. During the first few weeks after basic training she resented the manner in which she was supervised and so went AWOL. Some of her family finally found her and induced her to return to military control. Naturally, she was given company punishment; nothing severe, just enough to maintain discipline. She at once announced that she was being persecuted and again went AWOL.

That time the authorities tracked her down and brought her back, but not quietly. She fought, wept and had hysterics. As a precautionary measure, her company commander had her admitted to a hospital for observation and treatment by a psychiatrist. In a comparatively short time she was discharged as a psychoneurotic!

"She probably was psychoneurotic," said Colonel Still. "Certainly she doesn't sound normal."

"But," Colonel Price pointed out, "she received a disability discharge. She is eligible for and probably is now receiving a pension for serving her government. She was only in the service for a very short period of time and all she gave to her country was a lot of trouble. Is that just?"

The little Wac was getting intense, but Colonel Still maintained his composure.

"Before discussing justice," he said, "let us dispose of the diagnosis. I infer that you do not believe that such a diagnosis should be arrived at because of the young lady's conduct. So let me ask you this: A man contracts syphilis through his own personal acts and you call it syphilis. Very well! A surgeon, while operating upon a syphilitic patient becomes accidentally infected from the blood of that patient and comes down with the same disease. What would you call that?"

"It sounds O.K." I smiled admiringly at his adroitness. "But I side with Colonel Price. No matter what you call it, we still don't think the same consideration should be given to both the patient and the doctor."

Colonel Still sized me up for a brief second and then decided to be friends. "As a matter of fact," he grinned, "we don't either. So, what do we do about it?"

As the atmosphere drained off some of its latent hostility, Colonel Taylor for Air cleared his throat and said, "Now I'll tell one."

As we turned inquiringly, he began his story:

It started in a small mid-western town with a boy named Jones. He was the only son of a most refined widow and, as might be expected, made up her entire existence. The Jones boy never participated in the games of his schoolmates, nor went around with girls. He and his mother lived in a world of their own making.

Came the war and the Jones boy immediately went in for Air Cadets. Surprisingly enough, his mother not only approved but preened her pride in public.

The Jones boy went to Basic, next to Pre-flight, on to Primary and then—home! Washed out and discharged before ever flying a hundred miles. A broken, shaken thing. A psychoneurotic!

He and his mother retired within the seclusion of their isolated abode and closed the door of their lives to all others. The townspeople shrugged!

But in that same small town were the three Smith boys. Leaders in adolescent pranks, small-town wolfing and high school athletics, they, too, went out for wings, all within a year of each other.

The oldest died first; in the flaming wreck of a B-17 on a daylight raid over Germany. The other two did their best to avenge his death; the youngest piloting a bomber and the in-between flying fighter escort. Sometimes they flew the same mission, but alone or together they kept on flying, mission after mission. The decorations piled up and they could have returned home for a rest. But remembering their older brother, they volunteered to keep 'em flying.

Then came a day when the youngest's plane was torn by flak. It couldn't keep up, fell out of formation, a sitting duck! An enemy fighter closed in for the kill, but not before a friendly fighter swooped in from the opposite direction. It was one brother or the other!

The youngest boy got back to his base somehow, but he never flew again. He also returned to the same small mid-western town; a hero and—a psychoneurotic!

The townspeople didn't shrug that one off. At first they were puzzled and then mad. What kind of a deal was this? A little wet-nosed mama's boy goes out to do a man's job and comes sneaking back in no time at all to hide behind his mother's apron. So he's a psychoneurotic? O.K., what else could any-body expect?

But the Smith boys; that was something different. Two of them killed, with one being given the highest of all awards, posthumously! And the third, no older than the Jones boy, twice promoted and with three rows of ribbons! Him the same as the Jones boy? Not if they could help it!

"And, for that matter," Colonel Taylor concluded, "not if 'Hap' Arnold, Chief of the Army Air Forces, can help it, either."

I looked across at Colonel Still and he cast me an apologetic glance before speaking to Colonel Taylor.

"Did the Smith and Jones boys both have the same symptoms?" he asked.

"They both had neurotic reactions, but they certainly did not get them the same way," Taylor replied, defiantly.

"Then you want a distinction in diagnosis without a difference in disease!" Still flashed back.

"I think there should be a distinction," Colonel Price spoke up. "It doesn't seem right for persons who have broken down only after prolonged participation in battle to be called the same things as those who could not even endure preliminary training or early discipline in the Army."

"What would you suggest?" asked Still, with studious politeness.

"My suggestion is this," Taylor interposed, "divide them into three descriptive diagnoses according to their accomplishments; 'psychoneurosis,' 'operational fatigue' and 'combat fatigue'."

Still shook his head vehemently. "You can't apply an unscientific term or title to a scientific fact!"

A tenseness settled over the conference and I could see that we were headed for a long and bitter argument. Just then Mae, my ever efficient secretary, appeared with coffee. During its distribution, along with questions regarding sugar and cream, I did some fast thinking. When all were served, I grabbed the ball and started to run with it, but I didn't get far.

"Look," I started out, "Colonel Taylor and Colonel Price both believe there should be a distinction between three different classes of NP's; those who give up in the Zone of Interior, those who break down overseas without having been under fire and those who crack up in combat. Putting aside all technical aspects," I looked at Still, "what are the practical objections to such a plan?"

"Principally this," he leaned forward earnestly, "there is no difference in the general symptoms or type of treatment for any of them. When men are discharged for physical disability, there should be a proper medical diagnosis made, or else if they require treatment after discharge how would a doctor know what to treat them for?"

The little Wac Colonel's lips formed a word, and I thought it was "nuts," but aloud she asked, decorously, "Colonel Still, have you any idea how many psychoneurotics receiving a disability discharge have required medical attention after being separated from the service?"

"No," Still smiled back, "have you?"

"I do know this," she replied, "the average person believes that anyone discharged for reasons of mental ailments needs to be taken care of after leaving the service. Isn't that correct?"

No one would commit themselves but me. "That is a logical conclusion," I stated.

"Then it may interest you to know," she said, speaking to me, "that, of the thousands and thousands discharged for psychoneurosis, less than one percent have been considered by the medical department as incapable of caring for themselves. The remaining ninety-nine percent have been released in their own custody; meaning that they require no further care."

"I probably can give a reason for that," I replied. "The chief job of a psychiatrist is to discover what causes a neurosis and separate the patient from any conditions that bring it about. It's sort of like asthma or hay fever; find out what gives it to a person and the rest is easy. The same with psychoneurosis. Our Army psychiatrists have learned that in eight cases out of ten, the mere fact of being subjected to Army training is the main reason for the disorders, so the doctors get their patients discharged and that ends the need for any more care or treatment."

For the first time, Still and Taylor acted in accord. They closed in on me like a couple of Tiger tanks, their cohorts in full support. It was a free for all, but I kept throwing irrefutable facts and figures at them, and the little Wac Colonel was right in there pitching with me. What data I could not furnish, she had. There followed a hectic hour of heated argument before we exhaustedly called a truce for lunch.

"Let's get this straight," I said, when we had returned and all were in a better humor. "What Colonel Price and I are trying to point out to you is that all the undesirables, all the guys who can't take it, are being discharged from the Army as psychoneurotics, whether they are or not. It's not always the doctor's fault by any means, but that is what's going on, just the same. So the people in this country take a look at what we call psychoneurotics and jump to the conclusion that a psycho is pretty much of a bum. That is kind of tough on the real psycho who is a sick man and needs help. It is also going to reflect unfavorably on the profession of psychiatry. First thing you know, people will be ashamed to be seen going into a psychiatrist's office; they'll be sneaking in the back way, like going to a GU clinic."

"Furthermore," little Price added, "there is a certain amount of stigma attached to the diagnosis of psychoneurosis. It is turning out to be more punitive than beneficial because most employers in industry want to see a man's discharge before hiring him, and they are very reluctant to give a job to anyone discharged as a psychoneurotic. We are already receiving hundreds of appeals, asking that the reasons for discharge be changed."

"I do not doubt that," said Still, "but I would be very much surprised if any of them asked to have the discharge itself recalled in order that they could return to the service for the performance of full military duty."

"No," Price smiled, "we have not been confronted with that problem."

I said, "Let's look at it this way. There certainly are three classes of psychoneurotics we deal with. The first and greatest number are those who manifest symptoms of a more or less severe nature between the time they are inducted and before they go overseas. Then there are those who develop disorders after going overseas but either before or without being exposed to the stress of combat. And lastly, those who sooner or later get the battle jitters and cannot carry on any further. Is that correct?"

Everyone agreed that it was.

"Then let's take them up separately, starting with the first group. Since they obviously were psychoneurotics before coming into the Army and very quickly developed decided reactions just for being in the service, are we responsible for their disorders?"

"We are and we aren't," Still smiled.

"Granted," I said, "but should the people of this country be everlastingly saddled with the care and keep of those cases, just because the individuals were called upon to make some personal sacrifices for their country?"

"No!" was the unanimous reply.

"Then the first thing is to find a way to separate those in that category from the Army by means other than a medical discharge."

"That could be accomplished by a more liberal policy regarding separations for inaptitude," suggested Price.

"It could," I admitted, "but that was tried back in '42 and we immediately had more men going out than we had coming in on the draft."

"That was because we left it up to the commanders," she said, "who abused the privilege by getting rid of all but the very best. What I had in mind was leaving it in the hands of the doctors. But instead of leaving them only one recourse, a medical discharge, make available to them one other method, such as 'for the convenience of the government,' with no medical diagnosis required."

"And to whom would that apply?" asked Still.

"To any psychoneurotic with nervous disorders precluding his adaptation of adjustment to the military service."

"Provided, of course," Still stipulated, "that the individual was in no further need of medical attention for those particular disorders after discharge."

"That's fair enough," I said, and when Colonel Price agreed I went on. "The next question is, what do we do about the ones who give a reasonable amount of service to their country but break down after a year or more without having gone into combat?"

"That's a tough one," said Taylor. "I'd rather talk next about the boys who crack up in combat."

"O.K. Supposing you start it off," I said.

"What we want is a way to differentiate between the youngsters who have actually fought and the thousands of little Jones boys who are allergic to O.D. and get sick the minute they put on a uniform."

"I'm willing to go along with that," Still conceded, "so long as protection is given to the psychoneurotics who need medical attention, regardless of when, how or where their disorders developed. After all, when a man is sick he should have medical attention. My comparison of the doctor and the patient who both caught syphilis is what I am pointing at. Medical treatment is not dependent upon the origin of a disease but upon the disease itself."

"That, of course, is true in medical and surgical cases," I agreed. "But to me, the reverse seems to be the case with psychoneurosis because the disease itself is dependent upon a certain cause and you have to consider the basic cause as well as the disease itself if you are going to effect a cure!"

"To a certain extent that also is true," said Taylor.

"Then for practical purposes, why can't we do this?" I offered. "For those who get sick just because they are brought into the Army, we dispense with a medical discharge unless, in the opinion of a medical officer they will need further treatment after discharge for disorders brought about by induction and retention in the service."

When that was agreed upon by all present, Still advanced another proposition. "Then how about this? Initially, let the disorders of men who break down in battle be diagnosed as being caused by 'combat fatigue' for a certain period of time. If they recover sufficiently to either be returned to duty or discharged in their own custody, let there be no diagnosis of psychoneurosis. But if they do not recover sufficiently to be considered cured of their neurosis, give them the proper scientific diagnosis, regardless of subsequent disposition."

We all looked at Taylor, but before agreeing, he asked, "What about the men who have been overseas for prolonged periods, although not in combat? There are plenty of conditions, such as isolation on a lonely island, separation from families, long hours of flying patrol, and many others that can produce a neurosis. What are you going to do about them?"

"Why not divide all psychoneurotics into just two classes?" suggested the little Wac. "Those whose disorders are considered justifiable by a psychiatrist and those who are simply nervous in the service?"

The doctors were on her like a pack of wolves. Evidently there could be no diagnosis of a disease in accordance with the merits of the conditions under which the disease had been contracted. Reluctant to lose what ground we already had gained, I waded into the verbal deluge.

"Hold on," I almost shouted. "We've already agreed that the boys who are simply nervous in the service should be gotten rid of without a medical discharge, unless the case is severe and needs further medical attention. All we're interested in now is what to do about the ones whose disorders have been brought about by something more than just Army routine. Isn't that right?".

After a moment of cooling off, they all agreed that such was their understanding.

"Well, that's just about what Colonel Price was saying. Why not treat all the rest as either 'operational fatigue,' or 'combat fatigue' cases. Let those be temporary diagnoses for, say from six to eight weeks. By that time the man either recovers or else is called a psychoneurotic for keeps!"

It wasn't too good a solution, but it was the best we could arrive at.

"That may be all right for the future," Still agreed reluctantly, "but it isn't going to do much good with regard to the thousands of men already discharged."

"Perhaps the Veterans Administration will get that straightened out in due time," Price suggested.

"I'm afraid it will be years before they can get enough help to check up on all the psychoneurotic cases to see whether or not they should continue to draw pensions," reflected Still.

"And in the meantime," added Taylor, "Many of them will have become professional invalids."

"You think that if a psycho is paid for being psychoneurotic it would be a deterrent to his recovery?" I asked.

"Without being unethical, I think I can truthfully say that such is my belief," said Taylor.

I looked at Still but he smilingly refused to be committed.

"Well," I sighed, "that's a problem for the Veterans Administration. We have enough problems of our own without getting into their field of activity."

"Somehow," Colonel Price confided to me as the conference prepared to break up, "I don't feel that we have solved the problem as a whole."

"Colonel," I said, momentarily, putting my hand on her shoulder, "in my opinion, it is a problem that will never be solved, because it is the problem of human nature. All we can hope for is to find a solution that best fits our own part in trying to make the greatest number of people do their share in safeguarding the interests of our country. We have to do the best we can with what we get and no one can do any more."

The little Wac departed, still shaking her head. She was not entirely satisfied with what we had accomplished nor, for that matter, was I. For hours afterwards I sat thinking, trying to sort out and arrange in orderly manner all the various and conflicting sides of the picture. Like a one-man jury, I reviewed all the evidence and tried to come to a conclusion on what I, myself, believed. And, like many juries, I found that I could not agree with myself.

Then, late that night, I received orders. I was to appear in the Chief's office early next morning for final presentation of the results of my inquiry!

CHAPTER 13

THE PAY OFF

~~~~~~

THERE IS NO WAITING WHEN YOU HAVE AN APPOINT-
ment with the Chief. Naturally, I got to his outer office well
ahead of time, but on the tick of the clock I was ushered into
the presence of that grave yet understanding man who carried
so many burdens on his shoulders.

I would have stood at attention but he waved me quickly to
a deep leather chair.

"Well, Cooke," the corners of his eyes crinkled slightly,
"you've gotten around pretty much on this job, haven't you?"

"Yes, sir," I managed to say. Imagine me, with nearly thirty
years' service having trouble with my voice!

"Learn anything?" he smiled.

"Yes, sir," I said. "I found out a lot." But that seemed to be
as far as I could get.

"Tell me about it." There was no pressure in his voice or
any indication of impatience, although God knows how many
other weighty problems were awaiting his attention.

"Well, sir, I'm not a psychiatrist, so the best I can do is tell
the way this business of psychoneurosis looks to a plain, everyday line officer."

He nodded briefly. "That is why you were sent out, to get
the perspective of a non-medical officer. We know what the
specialists have said. Now supposing you tell me your views in
the same way you would if you were explaining the problem to
an assembly of junior officers and noncommissioned officers."

"In that case, sir, I would start out by saying there are four
groups to be considered."

205

"Four?" his eyebrows arched.

"Yes, sir. Psychotics, constitutional psychopaths, psychoneurotics and just damn deadbeats."

"Oh!" he smiled. "Very well, go on."

I continued. "The psychotics are commonly called crazy, usually have to be kept in an institution or locked ward and, under the law, cannot be held accountable for their acts. We have had comparatively few of these as compared to the overall number involved. Since only members of the medical profession are qualified to classify or treat them, I did not extend my inquiry into that field except as it pertained to the general picture."

"A wise decision," the Chief approved.

"Next come the constitutional psychopaths, or psychopathic personalities as the medical people are now calling them," I went on. "They are the persons who habitually break laws and regulations and get into trouble. They dislike taking orders and think they know better than the duly appointed authorities what's best. They are the outlaw type and are most likely to kick over the traces, get drunk and disorderly, do the most bitching and raise hell in general. They also are prone to be exhibitionists and want to do things differently from anybody else."

"I believe I have encountered some of them," the Chief smiled. "But tell me, are they fighters?"

"They are belligerent enough in attitude," I answered, "although it is mostly on the surface. Occasionally, no doubt, some of them have committed acts of individual heroism, but I don't think they go in much for group bravery. They would be more likely to excel at bushwacking or guerrilla operations. Their interest in personal reward or recognition certainly exceeds any sense of duty they might have. Also, as a general rule, they are a pain in the neck to commanders and a serious road block to discipline and morale."

"And how would you instruct your junior leaders to handle such individuals?" the Chief demanded.

"With determination and intestinal fortitude," I replied. "Those people will not recognize a leader less determined to require obedience than they are to do as they please. Also, their loyalty is only to a 'gang' or special group. Any appeal on a higher level than that is going to be wasted, if it doesn't arouse contempt. And last, although maybe the most important of all, anything one of them does well must be openly acknowledged, just as they must be jumped on like a ton of brick if they do any wrong."

The Chief ran the flat of a forefinger across his lips. "That might apply to the handling of any group of men."

"Yes, sir," I acknowledged, "because there's a bit of the psychopath in all of us. It's only when there's too much of it in any one person that there seems to be trouble."

He nodded understandingly and motioned for me to proceed.

"I don't think a junior officer would have much difficulty in recognizing a psychopath, if he knew what to look for, but a psychoneurotic is different. I'm not so sure I can explain just how to identify a psycho."

The Chief just waited quietly, and I saw that I had better make a try at it, anyhow. So I took a deep breath and started off. "The psychoneurotic sort of makes himself sick, without exactly knowing how or why he does it, or even without realizing it at all. He might be compared to a man who is allergic to something without knowing what it is, and breaks out with asthma, dermatitis and things like that."

"How does the allergy affect him?" asked the Chief.

"Well, sir, it makes him nervous. After a certain amount of pressure, his nerves upset some function of his body and then he is sick."

The Chief leaned forward slightly. "And what is it that those men are allergic to in the Army?"

I was a little apprehensive. "Mostly, they are allergic to the Army itself, and all that it stands for in time of war."

The Chief leaned back. "And what are you going to tell your junior officers is the remedy for *that?*"

"I'd start out by telling them some of the remedies that have already been tried."

"What are they?"

"The most popular one, at first, was to encourage some tough noncom to take each individual psycho out behind a latrine and beat the daylights out of him."

"Did that do any good?" the Chief asked calmly.

"Definitely not! It soothed the commander's ego, but it didn't increase the psycho's efficiency one little bit."

"What is the next one?" the Chief's chin tipped back to a more comfortable angle, as though he had all day to listen.

"Another solution offered, was to put all psychos into labor battalions and send them into the combat zone where they would take some of the same chances of being killed as the boys who were willing to fight."

"What happened to that idea?"

I shrugged. "It just died for lack of nourishment."

"Why?"

"For two reasons, sir. First, because the ones who suggested it were those who wanted to get rid of their psychos and they couldn't find any volunteers for taking over the job. Second, the

General Staff did not like it, <u>because that is what the Germans are reported as doing and the Staff</u> were quite sure the American people would be violently opposed to our doing the same thing."

The Chief nodded his understanding.

"However," I resumed, " we have adopted the idea to a certain extent in a modified form. Some of our overseas divisions are putting their psychos into companies or battalions under command of their division psychiatrists, and they are used to build roads and other jobs in the division area."

"Has it been effective?"

"According to certain psychiatric reports, it has been most effective." He regarded me under level brows for a short period before asking, "Then why isn't that the answer?"

"Sir," I replied, producing a tabulation of figures, "according to recent releases, it has been stated that from forty to fifty out of every hundred men suffering combat engendered emotional disturbances have been returned to duty within two days; ten to fifteen others were returned to duty after two weeks; thirty more improved sufficiently to be kept on non-combatant jobs; and even some of the rest stayed in the Army to render some kind of service."

"Is there anything wrong with those figures?"

The Chief's right hand raised slightly, as though about to reach for a telephone or buzzer, so I hastened to say, "They probably are quite correct. The trouble is, they refer only to 'combat engendered emotional disorders,' in other words, men who have cracked up in combat. No one actually considers them a problem except from a humane or sympathetic viewpoint. It is the other eighty to ninety percent which have been giving us the headaches."

A slight frown creased the Chief's forehead. "Could there possibly be that many others in comparison to the number caused by battle?"

"No, sir;" I held onto my courage by the seat of its pants because the frown suddenly became a thunder cloud, "I don't believe there could."

"Then what are you driving at?"

"Sir, we never had many psychiatrists in the Army before the war. In fact, I don't think one military person out of a hundred knew what the word meant. They don't know now, except they have come to believe it is some kind of a hocus-pocus, black magic business. And that's where my fourth group comes in— the dead beats. Our commanders and leaders didn't know what psychiatry was, and a lot of them didn't give a damn, but they soon put two and two together; psychoneurosis was a magic word! When pronounced by a doctor, the command was almost immediately rid of some undesirable character. Well, GI Joe figured that one out almost as soon. Most of the boys were too proud to take advantage of the opportunity, but plenty of them did, and the doctors, poor devils, were caught in between."

"But as doctors," the Chief puzzled, "who would put pressure on them?"

"Everyone," I stated, "from the division commanders, on down. Also, their friends and other officers with whom they ate, slept and did business, needled them every day."

"But under their Hippocratic oath, how could doctors justify being influenced into doing anything they did not believe was right?"

"Sir, they had taken another oath also, that of an officer in the Army. As such, they were subject to orders, and loyalty to their outfit was also a part of it."

The Chief shook his head disapprovingly, so I hastened on to add, "Another thing, sir, were the men themselves, the eight balls! Many of them were mild or borderline cases of what they purported to be. And a great many of the symptoms those men described themselves as having were of a psychiatric nature. Therefore, with the heat turned on from all directions it was not difficult for the doctors to convince themselves that the best thing for all concerned was to send those eight balls to a hospital where they could be observed by a psychiatrist."

"Then why didn't the psychiatrists screen out the dead-beats and return them to duty?"

"They tried, sir. At least at first. But it was sort of like throwing a rubber ball against a stone wall, it bounced right back in their faces! It requires from three to four weeks to put a patient through all the necessary clinics in a crowded and busy hospital before it can definitely be established that the man has no organic disease and for the psychiatrist to arrive at a diagnosis. By that time the man has gotten a taste of easy existence in a hospital and doesn't want to go back to duty. And his outfit certainly doesn't want him back!"

"But surely they were sent back anyhow, weren't they?"

"Yes, sir, but from being in an NP ward those men had learned a lot. Through observations and talk with other patients they knew the symptoms that most baffled the doctors. So, as soon as they were returned to duty those eight balls started riding the sick book again until pretty soon they were back in an NP ward, the problem of a psychiatrist."

"Then what kind of a solution to that problem did the psychiatrists finally arrive at?"

"A very simple one, sir, to wit: a medical discharge for physical disability."

The Chief folded his arms and gazed thoughtfully into space. Finally he heaved a sigh and asked, "Just how bad has the situation become?"

Referring to some previously prepared figures, I replied, "Sir, aside from the loss in manpower, current calculations indicate that not less than forty percent of all men drawing pensions for physical disability are NP cases. Certainly, not more than ten of that forty percent could possibly have seen combat. Right now, more than a hundred thousand men are drawing compensation because of being nervous in the service and the cost to our people is well up into the millions of dollars."

Shaking his head as though coming up after a sudden plunge into cold water, the Chief said, "It is a little late to do anything about the past, but what suggestions have you for those officers who may be confronted with these problems in the future?"

Since I had been asking myself that very question for several months, I was able to offer an answer. "Sir, if it were to be done over again, I would first suggest that all training be made progressive in accordance with the ability of each individual trainee. Under our present system, everyone gets the same amount of basic training and then, bingo! Out comes a soldier."

"You are wrong," the Chief spoke emphatically, "all training centers now have special battalions for those who cannot assimilate training in the required length of time."

"That is true, sir, but those units are usually filled with the dull and illiterate, and our psychos as a rule are neither. Even the majority of our eight balls are smart enough, in a precocious sort of way. Some of them might not be able to finish their training in the specified time, but some of them, as well as a great many who are not psychoneurotics, could finish in a much shorter period, only there is no incentive to do so."

The Chief made a brief penciled note before I continued. "As another preventive measure, I would suggest greater emphasis on expert classifications and assignments."

"We are already doing that, at the reception centers."

"Yes, sir, we are. But assignments to branch of service depend more upon physical than mental qualifications, which means that a man with a good body goes to combat troops whether or not that man has the guts necessary to take that body into battle."

After a brief moment of thought, the Chief said, "But I understand we have psychiatrists at the reception centers for that very purpose."

"We have, sir, and they do their best. But they see from one to five hundred men a day and have but a few minutes with each upon which to base a decision. And, unless they reject a man entirely, any notation on the man's record indicating psychoneurotic proclivities gives him his first step down the road towards a disability discharge. That is why my next suggestion would be to discontinue discharging psychoneurotics except in those cases where a psychiatrist was convinced that the patient would require further and continued care after separation from the service."

"What would you do with the others?"

"I'd put them all in units of their own, with a psychiatrist as consultant commander and adviser on therapeutic treatment. I would make those men perform some kind of work and insist upon their units being self-supporting as to housekeeping duties, and so forth. But above all, I would never let a single one of them get into a hospital except upon the explicit recommendation of a psychiatrist."

"Is that all?"

"No, sir, one more thing. I would insist that a practical course in psychology and the basic principles of psychiatry be included in the curriculum of every one of our Army schools and be given a very high priority. Last, but not least, I would then announce and adhere to a policy that any epidemic or excess number of psychoneurotic cases in a command would be accepted as prima facie evidence of inadequate leadership!"

The Chief regarded me quite seriously for a few moments, and then said, "I am afraid some of your ideas are a trifle idealistic and do not take into consideration the necessity of expanding a peacetime Army of professional soldiers into one a hundred-fold in size composed mostly of civilians. Particularly in an emergency when time alone is the major factor involved."

"Perhaps so, sir. And hindsight is always better than foresight. Nevertheless, those are the objectives I would set up and strive for."

The Chief nodded and his chair came forward. "Very well, put it all down for the record; not only for consideration now but also for the information of those who follow in our footsteps. Give them the opportunity to profit by any of the mistakes we may have made."

"Yes, sir," I saw that the interview was ended.

I got to my feet, saluted and started for the door.

"Oh, Cooke!"

"Yes, sir?" I halted, about faced and stood at attention.

His eyes appeared a little weary yet they both commanded and urged.

"It has occurred to me that you can help still more on this problem."

I waited anxiously.

"Whether you know it or not, you have acquired some very

broad knowledge on a practical level during the course of this inquiry."

"Yes, sir?"

"You also have a unique method of expression which I believe would be understood and appreciated by a great many people."

Not knowing how to answer that, I remained silent.

"It would not be right to have that information forever buried in the files of the War Department. When the necessity no longer exists for keeping these matters confidential, you owe it to our people to share your knowledge with them. Do you understand?"

I gulped. "You mean, sir, I am to write it up for publication?"

"I do," his eyes were compelling. "Can I rely upon you to do that?"

"Sir," my voice acted up, the same way as when I first entered his office, "I promise! I'll do it, or bust a gut trying!"

And—this is it.